R. A. Whitehead

STEAM
IS THE ESSENCE

To mark the Golden Jubilee (1987) of the Road Locomotive Society

Chris Lambert's "Steam Party" June 21, 1952, in his yard at Horsmonden.   [John H.Meredith]

Frontispiece: A steam idyll of deep summer, as the distant Bomford owned ploughing engine,
adapted for dredging on Harry Evershed's system, begins to draw in a loaded scoop of
his design, c.1920.

Other books by R.A.Whitehead
¶ denotes still in print

¶ *The Story of the Colne Valley* (jointly with F.D.Simpson)	Oakwood Press [Reprint]
Garretts of Leiston	Percival Marshall
A Century of Service	Eddison Plant
The Age of the Traction Engine	Ian Allan
A Century of Steam Rolling	Ian Allan
Steam in the Village	David & Charles
Garrett 200	Transport Bookman
Kaleidoscope of Steam Wagons	Marshall Harris & Baldwin
Kaleidoscope of Traction Engines	Marshall Harris & Baldwin
Wallis & Steevens - a History	R.L.S.
¶ *A Review of Steam Tractors*	R.L.S.
¶ *Austrian Steam Locomotives 1837-1981*	R.A.Whitehead & Partners
¶ *The Beloved Coast & the Suffolk Sandlings*	Terence Dalton
¶ *Jesse Ellis & the Maidstone Wagons*	R.A.Whitehead & Partners

R. A. Whitehead

STEAM
IS THE ESSENCE

A REVERIE ON STEAM IN THE LANDSCAPE

R. A. Whitehead & Partners
Tonbridge, Kent

1993

Fig,1   *Three stalwarts of the rolling trade c.1904. On the left Joseph de Mattos (Eddison Steam
Rolling Co), Jesse Ellis, and (right) John Allen. The Fowler roller belonged to the Oxfordshire
Steam Ploughing Co. (shortened to Oxford Steam Plough Co. when it became a limited
company), and had just been fitted with a Bomford scarifier (designed by Harry Evershed) the
operation of which is being demonstrated.*   [MERL]

Published by R.A.Whitehead & Partners
42, Hadlow Road,
Tonbridge, Kent TN9 1NZ

Cover: 6NHP Fowler compound general purpose engine threshing near Wallingford,
           Berkshire.

Photographs: Unless otherwise acknowledged all illustrations are from the collections
             of the Road Locomotive Society, or of the author. Illustrations from other
             sources are acknowledged individually.

Typeset in Times New Roman by J.E.Whitehead.

Printed and bound by Biddles Ltd., Woodbridge Park, Guildford, GU1 1DA

ISBN 0-9508298-2-X

Contents

Fig.2. The first public trial of an Allen scarifier in Oxford, undated, but probably early twenties. [Basil Harley]

Foreword

by the late B. Derek Stoyel Esq.

I was delighted when I was asked to write the foreword to this book. My pleasure is indeed a double one: in the first place I was closely associated with the Road Locomotive Society on its formation, and it had in fact been born in my house, and I have therefore always had a warm place in my affections for it. Having now reached the age when I can no longer participate in most of its activities, I am very pleased that I am able to play some small part in celebrating its Jubilee, as nothing had been further from my mind.

In the second place I am pleased because I feel flattered to be considered worthy to be associated, even in a minor way, with this work of my friend Robert Whitehead, who, with some training as an engineer, has a much more fundamental knowledge of steam engines than most of the early members and also has the relatively rare gift of writing. Further, he has been active in the Society over a long period. I can claim to have read more of his books than those of any other writer on this subject and once again the present book immediately impresses me by the broadness of his vision. His task has been to give a general survey of the development of the road locomotive since its birth, and particularly during the fifty years of the Society's existence.

As I have lived most of my adult life in West Kent, first at Orpington and latterly at Tunbridge Wells, I have known him as a near neighbour at Tonbridge for a long while and we have inevitably been familiar with many of the same engines. One of the pleasant features of the book is that it is liberally enlivened with anecdotes about engine owners and drivers, and as many of them were in Kent I have often known the individuals concerned and their engines, thus giving me a great personal interest in what he has to say about them.

Looking back on the youth of the Society, I think that perhaps the greatest encouragement that the early members ever experienced was when the late Chris Lambert asked to become a member. I remember very clearly that one day in September, 1934, one of my brothers and I drove from Surrey into West Kent in an effort to discover part of the engine population of the area, and one of the highlights of the day was a call at the yard at Horsmonden in which Christopher Lambert kept his engines. We asked permission to look at them and he was surprised that two young men should be so keen to examine them that they had come a distance to do so, although they had no practical experience of engines. After we had been shown round the yard he asked me to leave my address with him so that he could send me a list of all the engines that he and his father had ever owned - more than a hundred of them! This formidable list soon reached me in the post and from then onwards we maintained regular contact with one another. One day I mentioned the formation of the Society and Chris promptly asked if he could become a member. The Committee was inordinately proud and encouraged that a leading engine proprietor and engineer should wish to be associated with a group of callow amateur enthusiasts. He later became a collector of engines and during the last few years of his life he held an annual 'open day', thus paving the way towards the preservation movement and the ever popular steam rallies.

Another early memory, which, however, pre-dated the formation of the Society, was a meeting with the late Thomas Boughton of Amersham Common. He was a key figure in Buckinghamshire in much the same way as Chris Lambert was in Kent. I cycled to Amersham from New Malden where I then lived and on reaching the impressive yard of traction engines, I rather timidly sought out the proprietor to ask permission to look at them. His reaction was almost identical with that of Chris Lambert a few years later, one of pleased surprise at such a request from a young man with just an amateur interest in engines. He was a very charming man and had a profound knowledge of the individual features of the various engine manufacturers. He was very pleased when I was able to show him a few photographs that I had with me, and invited me to lunch so that he could give them a closer look. I have often regretted that the Society did not then exist as I am sure that he would have greatly enjoyed becoming a member and would have added materially to our standing.

Whilst much of the information in this book is naturally known to me as one of the original members of the Society, I have been surprised at the number of facts mentioned which I did not know before. Nearly every page gives evidence of the wide research which Robert has carried out with the capable assistance of his wife, Jean, and not only have they collected a vast amount of information but they have also been able to weld it into a comprehensive and continuous story with the utmost skill. I am quite certain that every member of the Society, whether already knowledgeable or a mere beginner, will find much to interest and inform him in the pages of this book.

Derek Stoyel
Tunbridge Wells

February, 1987.

Figs. 3 and 4. *Two of Derek Stoyel's photographs. They are (top) Ransomes, Sims & Jefferies No.25660 in September, 1935, threshing when owned by T.& F.Thompson, Culgaith, Cumberland, and (lower) Marshall 39218,* Lady Muriel, *seen during the same visit, at Melmerby, Cumberland, powering a stone crushing plant.*

Preface

For a Society to reach a fiftieth anniversary merits appropriate commemoration. It was a fortunate conjunction of events, therefore, that when the Road Locomotive Society attained its golden jubilee in 1987 the chance arose to purchase the surviving Burrell drawings. Their acquisition and placing in the newly constituted museum at Thetford was a very fitting tribute. Alternatively it had been proposed that the occasion should be marked by the publication of a book looking back over the era when road steam engines had been an accepted part of the landscape, liked by some but, it is to be feared, ignored or even actively disliked by most, a period when the arrival of the steam threshing set was as much taken for granted as the onset of autumn, or when an exceptionally heavy or out-of-gauge load was expected to have two road locomotives at the front and a third at the rear. The sight of the Kerrs' engines hauling a huge railway locomotive through Glasgow from Hyde Park Works to Stobcross Crane was an exciting spectacle even in an age when steam was not a rarity.

Accordingly this book attempts to evoke those days when steam was to be found in regular traffic and the problems and hostilities it experienced as well as the successes it enjoyed. As the sub-title implies, rather than a history, it is a reverie lingering over the atmosphere of the times. As my earlier work, *Steam in the Village,* was received very kindly it is hoped that this present work will be as acceptable.

Although for most of its commercial life the steam vehicle was hedged about with regulations and restrictions, reviled, harassed and, in extreme cases, actively persecuted, it did have a few disinterested well wishers who looked upon it favourably for its own sake, aside from any professional involvement with it. So few in numbers were they, and so scattered, that most of them scarcely realised that they were not unique. In the mid-thirties a small group of young men interested in the subject in London and the Home Counties did, more or less by chance, become aware of the fact that road steam formed a mutual interest. On 27th January, 1937, they met, under the chairmanship of Eric Preston, at Derek Stoyel's house in Orpington. From this meeting of eight men the Road Locomotive Society was formed to study and record the events of the rapidly declining use of steam on the road. The pages that follow may be looked upon, therefore, as an anthology of information gathered and preserved by members of the Society, including the author.

Robert A. Whitehead

Tonbridge,
Kent.
January, 1993.

Acknowledgements and Thanks

By its avowed objectives this book necessarily incorporates a liberal amount of the work of others supplemented by some original research of my own. To a considerable extent this involves 'scissors and paste'. It is difficult to see how matters could be otherwise. The sources of verbatim quotations are, generally, given in the text. Cordial thanks are extended to all those whose work is thus used, but much help has also been given by others, including John Creasey, Jonathan Brown, and the late David Phillips at the Museum of English Rural Life, (now the Rural History Centre),Reading, the Librarian and staff of the library of the National Motor Museum, the late Ted Dunn, Stan Jaques, the late Bill Newell, Ted Shirras and Edward Wood, and the following past or present members of the Road Locomotive Society, all of whom have contributed: - Les Burberry, Ronald Clark, Alan Duke, John Haining, Alan Martin, Stephen Mustill, Robert Pratt, Peter Smart, Frank Strange, and the following members, now deceased; Stan Cambray, Wilf Cole, Harold Darby, Frank Cheffins, Tom McTaggart, George Lea, Tom Paisley, John Peirson, (Rev) Reuel Stebbing, and Arthur Wedgwood.
To all members who have contributed, whether named or not, I am most grateful and offer my thanks accordingly.
I am also much indebted to three friends who are active showmen, namely, Allan Downs, George Irvin, and Benny Irvin, as well as to the late John (Jack) Denahy who drove engines for the Beach family, of which his widow, Selina, is a member.
Unless otherwise attributed illustrations are from the collection of the Road Locomotive Society or the author. Photographs and illustrations from other sources are individually acknowledged, and their owners are thanked for lending them.
I am particularly indebted to friends and members or past members who read in draft chapters dealing in aspects in which they are specialists - Philip Bradley (fairgrounds), Esmond Kimbell (threshing), Charles Lloyd and the late George Lea (haulage), and the late Bill Newell (timber hauling). Bill Love and the late Derek Stoyel each read it all, and Derek did me the further honour of contributing the foreword. To all of them I extend my heartfelt gratitude. It is a matter of sorrow that Derek did not live to see it published.
As has been the case with my previous ventures into writing, Jean, my wife, has taken part in the researching and correlation of the facts behind the manuscript and has assisted in its shaping. My son-in-law, Michael Walters, joined in some of the research and has read and commented upon the manuscript.

Chapter 1

Forerunners

Steam is firmly esconced in the generation of electric power but only in China and India does it play a significant part in direct rail traction whilst it has been displaced from road transport and is close to being displaced from the sea. The superior passenger comfort of a steamship is dearly bought because of the space taken up by its boilers, condensers and stokehold. The bulk of the boiler, and the supply of water needed for evaporation always were and remain the main problems, also, for the designer of a self-moving engine. The fundamental theme of the history of the development of steam traction has been the creation of sufficiently compact steam generators. The nearer this basic problem has come to solution the more importance has been attached to thermal efficiency.

Thermal efficiency was not a dominant consideration, however, in the design of atmospheric engines in the eighteenth century. Doubtless the owner of a coal mine deemed it a sufficient stride that the invention had provided a machine that enabled him to drain his pit by burning unsaleable smalls and waste. The boiler of such an engine was not a pressure vessel but a large enclosed kettle providing steam at atmospheric pressure that filled the cylinder void subsequently to be condensed to enable the pressure of the atmosphere on the other side of the piston to do the work required. So long as the fuel used under the boiler had no cash value it hardly mattered whether or not it was used wastefully in the thermal sense as the cost of using it came down simply to the wages of the stokers.

In other industries, however, the case was altered. To a group of Cornish mine adventurers having to bring their coal by sea to the nearest port, to load it by hand, and to transport it by horse and cart to their boiler house, the search for greater fuel economy was a pressing financial matter in which the introduction of the separate condenser patented and jealously guarded by Boulton & Watt, enabling the steam to be condensed without cooling the cylinder, was an important advance of design. The wording of the patents and the construction placed upon them by the courts made it extremely difficult for an effective and economical engine to be built by others without infringement. Notwithstanding this formidable barrier those involved with the management of Cornish mines made persistent and sustained efforts to improve the thermal efficiency of their engines by methods that did not incur payment of royalties to Watt. Crude infringement was resorted to by many but Watt was a determined litigator and pursued the offenders through the courts. Others, therefore, looked for methods of improvement by way of channels not blocked by Watt's patents.

It was in this endeavour that the brilliantly inventive mind of Richard Trevithick (1771-1833), the 'Cornish Giant' of Tom Rolt's felicitous phrase, made its first mark. Initially he set about raising the efficiency of the Watt type engine albeit in the face of implacable hostility from the patentee but in 1796, when Watt's patents had only four years to run, Trevithick found himself on the receiving end of an injunction over an engine he had erected at Ding Dong mine (near St.Just) in alleged infringement of the Watt patents. This seems to have been the final spur to the development of his high pressure engine in which the boiler was a true pressure vessel, rather than a kettle, and the exhaust was to atmosphere instead of to a condenser.

The use of Watt's atmospheric engine for mine winding was of an elephantine clumsiness that Watt had attempted, with some success, to improve with his sun-and-planet engines.Once Trevithick had reduced his high pressure engine to workable form it presented a power source that was not only more economical of space and easier to handle and erect but also considerably cheaper. The first examples were put to work about 1799 and about thirty were made in all.

The restless mind of their originator soon turned to using the same principles to drive a road carriage. This was not the first, coming as it did after Cugnot's three-wheeled tractor in Paris in 1769 and William Murdoch's model road locomotive of 1782, but it may well have been an original invention as Trevithick stated that he had not heard of Murdoch's model - though Murdoch's son said that he had - and he had probably no knowledge of Cugnot. Certainly it exhibited considerable differences from Cugnot's engine and many from Murdoch's. After experimenting with a model made for him by his wife's brother-in-law, William Wood, Trevithick embarked upon a full size machine, begun in the autumn of 1800 but not

Fig.5. A conjectural representation by Feldhaus (1911) of Trevithick's design for a steam threshing machine.

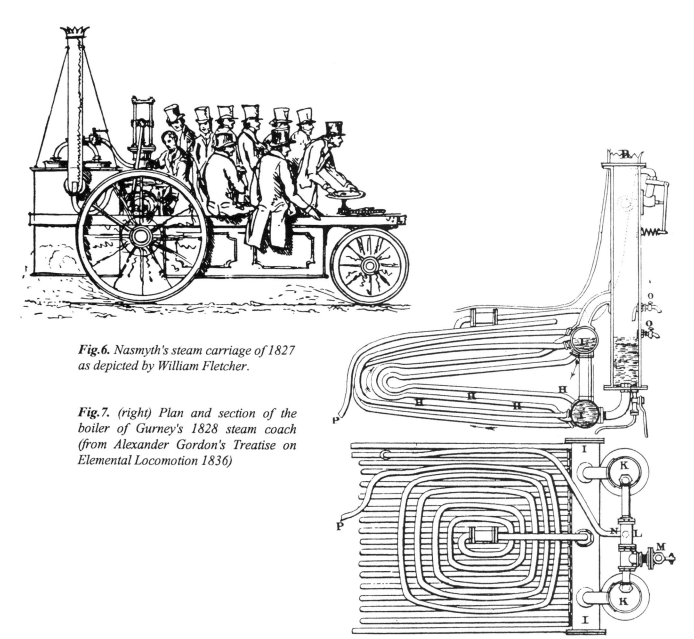

Fig.6. Nasmyth's steam carriage of 1827 as depicted by William Fletcher.

Fig.7. (right) Plan and section of the boiler of Gurney's 1828 steam coach (from Alexander Gordon's Treatise on Elemental Locomotion 1836)

completed for over a year. In a trial on the 1 in 20 slope of Beacon Hill, Camborne, the boiler proved unable to provide steam fast enough to keep the engine supplied and after an initial run up the hill the carriage stalled. On being taken onto the level turnpike road it met a similar fate. Retried after Christmas it suffered a small mishap, which caused the discouraged crew to push it into a building, with a fire still in it, though, as it turned out, not enough water. The water boiled away, the boiler overheated and set fire to the wooden framing of the vehicle and the machine was reduced to scrap.

Despite this setback a second carriage was constructed, the engine and boiler of which were made at the Hayle Foundry, and the bodywork in London by William Felton of Leather Lane, and completed and tried in the summer of 1803. A number of runs were made in the Camden area with some practical success but little public acclaim. Soon, however, he received public notice of an unwelcome kind when the boiler of one of his engines, employed on pumping out the foundations of a building at Woolwich, exploded, killing four men, Though the explosion happened from a cause that was subsequently to lead to many other mishaps, namely loading the safety valve, Boulton and Watt, by then his inveterate enemies, saw to it that the accident received the maximum publicity, with the worst construction placed upon the circumstances. Whether because of this denigration or from his discouragement at the lack of interest attracted by the road carriage Trevithick seems to have abandoned the latter from about that time. Ostensibly the venture had been successful in that, for the first time, a carriage was moved by steam, as opposed to animal, power but one must beg leave to doubt whether a vehicle of this type with its boiler shell of cast iron (although the internal return flue was wrought iron) could ever have been made commercially viable. One would have expected it to have been defeated by the combination of its weight and the problem of keeping it in repair under the pounding it received from the road.

Whether or not the carriage would have had a future had it been developed further is a question that can be answered only by the reader's imagination as, by the time the demonstration had been given, its designer had been drawn away to another project, namely the construction in 1803 of the celebrated Penydaren tramway locomotive in partnership with Samuel Homfray of the Penydaren Ironworks in Glamorganshire. In the next nine years Trevithick, having moved to London, involved himself in a multiplicity of ventures, - steam dredging in the Thames; his circular railway and steam locomotive near Euston Square; the making of rivetted tanks; the driving of a tunnel under the Thames , - culminating in a near fatal illness which, in turn, helped to bring about his bankruptcy and led to his return to Cornwall. There, in 1812, he once again undertook a task directly in the line of our narrative when he designed a small fixed engine for driving a threshing machine on the estate of Sir Christopher Hawkins, Bart., M.P. at Trewithen. This engine worked until 1879 when it was dismantled and taken to London where it survived to become part of the Science Museum collection. Of a second example made for his patron, Lord Dedunstanville, for his estate at Tehidy Park only the boiler survives. Further examples were undoubtedly made on the evidence of letters exchanged with J.U. Rastrick of Stourbridge, builder of many of his engines, quoted by Trevithick's son, Francis, in his biography of his father, but no part of them has been preserved.

Contemporaneously with these he was working on the idea of making portable engines. The fixed agricultural engines weighed only about 15cwt. so that apart from the awkwardness of their physical arrangement there was nothing impracticable about the idea of turning one of them into a portable, though there is no conclusive evidence that it was done apart from the oft quoted letter he wrote from Camborne on March 10, 1812, to Sir Christopher Hawkins in which he says:

"I am now building a portable steam whim on the same plan to go itself from shaft to shaft, the whole weight will be about 30cwt. and the power equal to twenty-six horses in twenty-four hours".

The inference here is that he had already made a portable engine and had gone on to consider means of making it self-propelling. From Camborne he wrote to Rastrick on January 26, 1813:

"I wish you to finish that engine with boiler, wheels, and everything complete for ploughing and threshing, as shown upon the drawing, unless you can improve upon it. There is no doubt about the wheels turning around as you suppose, for when that engine in Wales travelled upon the tramroad, which was very smooth, yet all the power of the engine could not slip around the wheels when the engine was chained to a post for that particular experiment."

Unfortunately in editing and publishing these letters Francis Trevithick tidied up and sanitised his father's unconventional, though expressive, grammar and his even more original spelling, so that although his father's ideas probably come over well enough, the impact of his impetuous personality is suppressed.

Other things, at this point, seem to have crowded out agricultural engines from Trevithick's notice. The fatal ease with which a new project could lure away his attention before enterprises already in hand had been established and consolidated meant that he achieved neither the success nor the rewards that would have surely come his way had he possessed the personality of, say, James Watt, able to discipline himself into setting up an orderly business with a partner of ability and integrity and competent assistants.

Had Trevithick continued with the development of portables and self-movers, it seems likely that the traction engine would have been on the scene earlier, but as it was he never returned to farm engines. Despite the fact that financial success commensurate with his ability eluded him the sheer range of his talents astounds. In Britain he was the first to build a full scale road vehicle propelled by means other than animal power. Habituated as we are to motor transport, we do not take in fully what an astonishing change this was. On the citizen of the 1800's, however, the impact was as epoch making, in its fashion, as the first voyage in space. No longer was land transport restricted by the limitations of animals just as after Gagarin's space ride man was no longer bound by gravity to the planet of his origin. Steam traction, mostly on railways, transformed the last century as the internal combustion engine in road and air transport has revolutionised this one.

From the time Trevithick abandoned his steam carriage project about 1805 activity seems to have subsided until 1821 when Joseph Bramah was noted as working on a steam coach to the designs of Julius Griffiths of Brompton. This vehicle appears to have existed for several years and to have had various styles of bodywork - a double barouche, an omnibus, and a wagon for goods - but probably never reached the stage of being a working proposition. It has two claims on our attention. It is the first recorded mechanical road vehicle intended for carrying goods and the first to have had a water tube boiler.

About the time (1827) that the Bramah coach/wagon finally expired James Nasmyth, later the inventor and patentee of the steam hammer, built an eight seater steam coach in Edinburgh at the request of the Scottish Society of Arts. Having demonstrated its working to the satisfaction of his patrons he turned to other pursuits that seemed to him likely to be more remunerative and the steamer was scrapped.

While it may not be entirely true to say that the stream of steam coach development dried up between 1805 and 1821, it could be said to have run underground with little overt activity. A link between Trevithick and later events exists, however, in the person of his fellow Cornishman, Goldsworthy Gurney. There is no direct evidence that he and Trevithick were acquaintances but it is recorded that Gurney met Trevithick's friend Davies Gilbert when staying at St.Erth during his holidays from school. Gurney was born in 1793 so would have been only about ten years old at the time Trevithick's carriage came to its untimely end, but to have seen it moving would have been a memorable event, inspiring to a potential inventor.

Whether or not the connection is more than a fanciful idea it is a fact that from the time of his arrival in London in 1820 or from soon afterwards Gurney was interested in self-propelled carriages. After a brief dalliance in 1823 with a proposal to use gaseous ammonia as the working fluid in the engine of a coach he turned to steam and completed his first coach in 1825. Initially distrusting the ability of simple adhesion to transmit the power of the engine to the road he did so by iron legs or 'propellors' alternately thrust out and retracted by the piston strokes leaving the wheels as load carriers. In his second coach he used these propellors as a standby only and in the third omitted them altogether.

Gurney was a consequential and bombastic man unpopular with his contemporaries who were exasperated by his vociferous self-praise and by the extravagant and often unjustified claims he made for his steam vehicles. To some extent this has caused the undoubted merits of some points of his designs to be overlooked. They all exhibited great originality. To keep a sense of proportion it must be remembered that they were the contemporaries of the early Hackworth locomotives on the Stockton and Darlington Railway and ante-dated the Rainhill trials on the Liverpool and Manchester Railway.

His boiler, best understood by reference to the drawing, (Fig.7) consisted of two horizontal drums one above the other linked by tubes in the shape of a letter U laid on its side, the lower part of them forming the firegrate. At each end the horizontal drums were linked to vertical drums which acted as steam domes. The long steam pipe from the dome to the front driving position and back to the undertype engine amidships must have been the means of the steam losing a great deal of heat. The engine was double high pressure using 9 inch diameter cylinders, the stroke being 18 inches, very long for a road vehicle. It drove a cranked, unsprung rear axle, which cannot have promoted a comfortable ride, and was fitted with an undeveloped form of link motion reversing gear capable of being actuated via a system of cables from the driving position but giving no possibility of variable cut-off. Steering was by means of a front lock, as in a horse-drawn coach, but with a tiller operated fifth wheel to activate it.

This coach did a number of quite long journeys, the most reported of which was one from London to Melksham and back. Despite these feats and its creator having described it as "perfect" it never, in fact, passed beyond the stage of experiment. With the advantage of hindsight one can suggest design features that defeated it. Like most early steam coaches, it worked at a low boiler pressure (variously reported at between 70 and 120p.s.i.) and in the days before superheat this in conjunction with the long steam pipe must have meant that the steam arrived at the cylinders wet and at a pressure further diminished to a serious degree. Since the reversing gear gave no possibility of expansive working these features of design must have made the coach very heavy on water and it is, indeed, reported to have been so. It was also given the reputation of "drawing its water", i.e. priming, but the design of the boiler does not look prone to such troubles and the wet running may simply have been the result of the initial low pressure in combination with condensation in the steam pipe. Despite its problems, on the return journey from Melksham the coach is said to have made the run of 84 miles in 9½ hours. If accurately reported, this was a very creditable performance for the coach and a remarkable endurance trial for its crew and passengers.

After this coach Gurney turned to making the light, relatively fast, steam tractors which he termed 'drags', adhering in the boiler and engine arrangements to the broad principles of the carriage. Sir Charles Dance used three of these drags in 1831 to establish a four times daily service between Gloucester and Cheltenham (9 miles) in a running time varying between 45 minutes and one hour. In just under four months of operation (February 27 to June 22) 3 640 running miles were logged. The service was soon up against the trustees of the turnpike who hindered its progress by ordering the coating of the road with thick layers of loose stone. On June 23 the drag in use broke its cranked axle and the service was suspended, never to be resumed. Colonel Macerone, Gurney's contemporary and one of his foremost detractors, remarked that it took the unceasing efforts of the Company engineer and three very skilled mechanics to keep one drag at work out of the three. It was said that they were made exactly alike to prevent this circumstance becoming obvious to observers.

It is worth remarking, however, that it took an effort on a comparable scale to keep Hackworth's stud of locomotives in working order on the Stockton and Darlington Raiway's coal trains, though there, at least, abundant traffic was to be had as an incentive to keep them at work. If one accepts as authoritative the later testimony of Sir Frederick Bramall, as there is every reason that one should since he was not only an eminent engineer but had been present as a youth at the time the drags were running and was, moreover, an acute and interested observer of what happened to steam on the road, the fare-paying public held back from Dance's enterprise and it was this, coming on top of the mechanical problems and the hostility of the turnpike trustees, that brought the enterprise to an end.

Undeniably the mechanical problems were severe. Contemporary technology was not able to satisfy Gurney's demands upon it. A constant problem was failure of the boiler tubes, almost entirely the result of the deficiencies of tube making techniques at the time. The cranked axle, without the availability of steel, was also a vulnerable item. Even a decade later wrought iron cranked axles on railway locomotives were still very suspect, whilst the fact that the axle of a Gurney drag or coach was unsprung would have accentuated the hammering imposed both upon it and upon the coach passengers. However, these problems of technology and metallurgy applied equally to the contemporary railway steam locomotive despite which by the mid-eighteen thirties it had become an unassailable commercial proposition. By that time few any longer talked of working railways with horses or endless ropes. Only the atmospheric system remained a competitor and that not for very long. The existence of a large demand for railways and the availability of large capital resources had stimulated the activities of builders and designers into achieving this result.

It is interesting, therefore, to speculate upon why the same pace of development did not apply to steam coaches. They suffered, in the same way as the did the railway, the opposition of the entrenched horse lobby. Unaccountably, however, the turnpike trusts, who were implacably against railways, were just as vehemently opposed to steam road vehicles. Dance's service from Gloucester to Cheltenham, a similar

Fig.8. John Scott Russell's steam carriage and tender, one of six built by the Grove House Engine Works, Edinburgh, for use in the service run in 1834 over a 7-mile route from Glasgow to Paisley. (W.Fletcher)

Fig.9. Cross-section through the engine compartment of a Scott Russell carriage. (W.Fletcher)

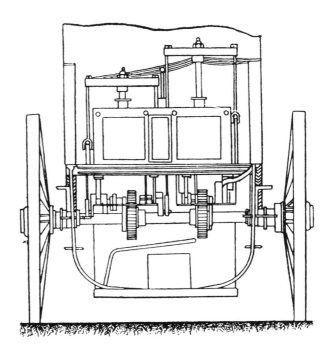

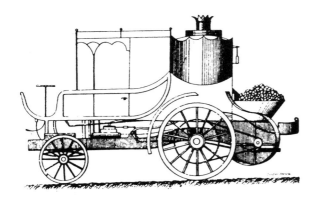

Fig.10. The second of the two steam carriages built by Squire and Macerone during their partnership of 1831-34

service in 1834 between Glasgow and Paisley using coaches designed and built by John Scott Russell, and Walter Hancock's bus service in London all met with unrelenting enmity. Why the turnpike trustees should have been so uniformly against steam road traction is, to the author, inexplicable. A successful development of the coaches would have preserved traffic on the roads at a time when it was in imminent danger of loss to the railways and saved the trusts from the extinction which overtook them in mid-century. Coaching inns, too, though they would have lost their revenue from horse coaches, might have kept their clientele and have replaced the lost income by coaling and servicing steam coaches. Parliament in the 1830's, moreover, was not hostile to road steam which received a remarkably sympathetic hearing at the hands of Parliamentary committees; there was no existing legislation against it and it was accorded reasonably even-handed treatment from the Government. By contrast, the growing system of railways had to face the vehement opposition of many of the greater and lesser landlords of the countryside who had a powerful influence on Parliament and Government, though, as events showed, not a decisive one. In these circumstances road steam might have been expected to have had the edge over railways. The opposition it faced was no worse than that encountered by the railways, and it did not have to incur the capital costs of building its own permanent way or stations. In explaining why it did not surge ahead one has to accept Sir Frederick Bramall's explanation may have been the right one, namely that public demand for passenger traffic was not there and could not be won. However, there was one factor more. Steam on the road aimed largely at passengers and mostly at those who could afford coach travel. Railways, by contrast, aimed to become carriers of minerals and goods on a considerable basis and to provide passenger transport for a much larger percentage of the public, albeit initially in patronising and degrading conditions so far as the third class traveller was concerned. Furthermore, railways offered the promise of greater speed, not, as one recent author has suggested, ten times that of a road steam coach but at least double, and possibly treble.

The protagonists of the steam carriage were not easily put to flight. For some time John Scott Russell defied the efforts of the turnpike trustees to put him off the road in Scotland. Having a pair of 12 inch by 12 inch cylinders his coaches were powerful machines which could keep going through the dragging layers of loose stone topping laid to hinder them, but the service ended with the death of three people in a boiler explosion, probably brought on by racking of the frame after the collapse of a wheel through excessive strain. The surviving coaches seem to have continued to exist for a long while. G.Lavergne (*The Automobile* 1901) stated that one ran as late as 1857 but he was writing forty-four years after the event. A more or less contemporary Gurney vehicle owned by Sir George Cayley was reported to have been involved in an accident as late as 1840.

Another durable steam carriage man of the eighteen-thirties was Colonel Macerone. In association with John Squire from 1831 to 1834 he built two workable steam carriages which were sent abroad, to Brussels and to Paris respectively, under the agency of a man named Azada (or Asda) by whom he was defrauded of monies due to him. Macerone himself was argumentative and litigious, always at odds with others in the steam carriage field - his former partner Squire, Gurney, Anderson, and such others as he considered had got in his way. A later Macerone coach, destined for the General Steam Carriage Company, was built by J.T.Beale in East Greenwich, London, and tested by him in 1840. The following year the General Steam Carriage Co. were noted in the *Mechanics Magazine* as making daily trips from the York and Albany Hotel, Regents Park, to Manor House, Tottenham, with a steam carriage that may quite possibly have been this Beale-built Macerone vehicle, though described as "Mr. Squire's Steam Carriage". This latter does not, as first might appear, disqualify it from being the carriage built by Beale as the Squire and Macerone partnership enjoyed an on-off relationship, and 1841 was an 'on' year. Two years later when Squire patented his design of boiler for steam carriages they were decidedly at loggerheads again with Macerone shrill in print with denunciations of his erstwhile associate's alleged infringements of his (Macerone's) patents.

The rapid advance of the railway by the eighteen-forties had thoroughly undermined whatever prospects the steam coach had ever had, a fact not lost on Macerone, an intelligent man despite his ebullience. The outburst against Squire seems to have been his last public pronouncement on steam carriages. After his departure from the scene the principal contender was Francis Hills of Deptford Ironworks, a modest and, on the whole, successful builder of private steam carriages. His achievements included a run from Deptford to Hastings and back in a day, but the trip required the services of a crew of three (the same as a railway train) to carry nine passengers. Probably the last of the traditional steam carriage men was Sir

Fig.11.
Crompton's
Bluebelle.

James Anderson of Buttevant Castle (Ireland), a persistent experimenter devoid of practical success. Of the thirty carriages he ruefully admitted to having had built not one performed well enough to justify a public demonstration, yet still he laboured on and one must admire his dedication.

By mid-century the vision of building a mechanical stage-coach for long distance travel had vanished. Whereas steam coach builders had had merely their aspirations for future traffic dashed by the steam train the whole complicated economy of horsed long distance road transport - goods and passenger - had been tumbled into total ruin by it. Coach lines were discontinued, stables were empty, inns ruined, turnpike trusts tottering to insolvency. As the prospect of transporting long distance passengers by road steamers faded the practical endeavours to promote the use of steam on the road became transmuted on the one hand into the incipient traction engine industry, and on the other into the designing of lighter, faster passenger carriages for private use, pointing the way, half a century on, to the coming of the motor car. In the designing of passenger-carrying vehicles rococo figures like that of Macerone yielded place either to gifted amateurs like Robin Grenville, trained, with his friend Churchward, in locomotive engineering in the shops of the South Devon Railway but diverted into the life of a country gentleman with no need to practise his profession, or else to men like Amos Richardson, machine shop proprietors, workmen who had made their way into management, or tradesmen of relative affluence such as Inshaw. However, such attempts to categorise are easily overturned. Where does one classify Richard Tangye, a founder member of a partnership internationally known for fixed steam plant, pumps, and hydraulic machinery on a huge scale that doubtless would have gone on to private steam carriages on a similar scale had not the operation of the 1865 Locomotives on Highways Act stifled the running of his prototype *Cornubia* steam car on the English roads. Or again there was Isaac Watt Boulton, whose working life at Ashton-under-Lyne was devoted to the repairing, hiring out, and even, on rather rarer occasions, actually building contractors' railway locomotives, but whose private amusement was building and running a series of seven small steam carriages of his own design that lasted many years and involved him in a succession of brushes with the constabulary and magistrates.

Though the Grenville steam carriage was still in regular use by the owner twenty years after it was built and, indeed, still exists in working order, to keep it running required the services of his faithful retainer Noble on the rear manstand, fulfilling the part of stoker mechanic, in circumstances that at the very least can be described as adverse. In just the same way the steam carriage built by Thomas Rickett of Castle Foundry, Buckingham, for the progressive Earl of Caithness made its now celebrated journey from Inverness over the Ords of Caithness to Barrowgill Castle near John O'Groats driven by the Earl from the passengers' bench seat at the front but with its creature requirements attended to by its builder exposed on the stoker's perch at the rear. Without doubt they, and others like them, were soundly engineered machines, probably with Grenville's in the lead because of the thought which had gone into making very strong road driving wheels on the basic principles of the Mansell type railway wheel.

One must agree, nevertheless, with the conclusion of the late Anthony Bird that "the Grenville and other steam carriages of its time were only one-off experiments", very well adapted to give satisfaction to the well-to-do men, imbued with the pioneering spirit and a taste for steam, by whom they were built or commissioned but never destined to capture the hearts of the majority of 'carriage folk'. Into this group falls the celebrated figure of Lieutenant, later Colonel, Rookes Evelyn Bell Crompton. Crompton began to build himself a private steam vehicle in 1861 when he was a schoolboy of sixteen but the project remained on a basis of more or less continuous experiment, complete enough to run under its own power but not effective in performance. In 1863 he worked for a spell at Doncaster Works under Archibald Sturrock but in 1864 abandoned railway service for the Army, and as Ensign Crompton of the Rifle Brigade arrived in India complete with his steam car. One gathers he was not straitened for cash. Life in India as as officer, even of junior rank, allowed a considerable amount of leisure, enabling Crompton to utilise the engineering experience he had gained at Doncaster to improve his car in the Army workshops and to turn it into an effective runner. About this time he named it *Bluebelle*. Upon reading of the rubber tyres patented by R.W.Thomson in 1867, with which he proceeded to equip his three-wheeled road steamers, Crompton wrote to him, reportedly in the hope of obtaining a set for *Bluebelle* at a competitive price, and from this prosaic beginning a deep affinity developed between the importunate young officer and the crippled inventor. Crompton was fired by his acquaintance with Thomson to broach with Lord Mayo (Viceroy of India from 1868 until his assassination in 1872) the subject of steam road trains for India, and later played a major part in the development of the electricity generating industry in this century. The subject of the road trains is dealt with a little further on in the chapter.

Two other cars call for mention. The first was designed by W.O.Carrett of the firm of Carrett, Marshall & Co. Ltd. in 1861 for one of the Salts of Saltaire near Bradford - sources differ as to whether it was Sir Titus or Mr. George Salt. The car was effectively a three-wheeled undertype gear driven steam tractor, with locomotive type boiler and seats for ten. As it weighed five tons it was larger than the tractors later permitted under the 1896 Act. The owner tired of it, perhaps because of the hampering effect of police activity upon his freedom of operation, and it eventually came into the hands of George de Vigne, the well-known and whimsical builder of Upper Thames boats and launches. Irritated at being stopped by the police when proceeding at what he looked upon as merely a sensibly brisk pace he is said to have fixed a dummy hose onto the vehicle and provided firemen's helmets for his friends, with efficaceous results - he was no longer stopped. Somewhat later he entered a small steam bus of his own design in the 1895 motor show which, on the evidence of the drawing of it published in *The Engineer*, would have been adorned by a figure head. Sad to relate it did not turn up.

The second car requiring mention is that designed by Alfred F. Yarrow and his friend J. B. Hilditch (aged 19 and 18 respectively). This pair of prodigies had already, when a year younger, become deeply versed in steam cultivation and ploughing to the extent that Yarrow at 18 had chaired a meeting of the Civil & Mechanical Engineers Society at which his younger partner had delivered an address on that subject. Their restless ingenuity had not long remained content with steam for working the land and had turned to steam cars. The Yarrow and Hilditch car was a four-wheeler but with a very narrow rear track which they claimed made it unnecessary to incorporate a differential gear, the absence of which was actually a retrograde steep despite saving money. The twin cylinders drove the rear wheels direct and as the axle was sprung this, in turn, produced complications in the valve gear. The two young men formed the Yarrow & Hilditch Patent Steam Carriage Company but the actual manufacture was undertaken in the works of William Cowan at Greenwich. Cowan who seems to have taken a close personal interest in the project drove the car from the works to South Kensington for the 1862 Exhibition, at which, to his chagrin and that of its designers, it was passed over in the awarding of the medals. Yarrow characteristically made light of this, remarking that the judge of the carriage class thought it an engine and the judge of the engines believed it to be a carriage, but, despite the joke, he was probably disappointed The car made many runs in its home territory at Bromley, Kent, or from Cowan's works, one taking it as far afield as Horsham, Sussex. Cowan, who had graduated from the position of a contractor to that of trusted co-worker, recorded having done a run of six miles in 22 minutes and the police appear to have turned a blind eye to its activities in the hands of its owners, well liked and affluent young men, until an unfortunate incident in Bromley in which a mounted policeman, encountering the car at night, was thrown and broke his leg. After this the car was discreetly sold to a buyer in Ireland. Yarrow's biographer said that they realised by that time that there was no market for steam cars.

Yarrow and Hilditch combined an interest in both steam carriages and heavy haulage or agricultural steam vehicles not seen in this country in the sixty years since Trevithick, whose early engines for use on farms had not initiated the widsread use of steam in agriculture that, coming to the market at a time when grain prices were still high as a result of the Napoleonic wars, might have been expected. Why they failed to do so can only be speculated upon. No doubt scepticism and a distrust of innovation had a part to play as did the fact that corn, priced at the record figure of 126s. 6d. per quarter in 1812, the year of Trevithick's portable, fell rapidly in price with the end of the war against France and the subsequent settlement of European boundaries reached at the Congress of Vienna in 1815. There can be little doubt also that Watt's malevolent whispering campaign against high pressure steam and the assiduous reporting of explosions of high pressure boilers that did occur must have had their effect on farming opinion. So too did the fear of Luddite type reprisals on farmers adopting labour-saving methods. Such reprisals in corn growing areas often took the form of rick-burning. The wholesome dread of fire whether by arson or accident was seldom far from a farmer's mind. With no better means of fire-fighting available to him than the chain of buckets from a pond or stream his reluctance to introduce a potential fire source in the sparks and cinders of an engine can be readily understood. All these considerations apart, however, the engines offered by Trevithick, though workable in the hands of the enthusiastic pioneers for whom they had been built, were not sufficiently adaptable or movable for them to make proselytes to the cause of steam from the general run of farmers beset by the doubts and problems outlined above.

Fig. 12. A double drum ploughing engine designed by Yarrow and Hilditch, and built by Coleman of Chelmsford.

Fig.13. An Aveling & Porter portable threshing. (MERL)

14

Consequently development of portables was not rapid. Nothing is recorded between 1812, the date of Trevithick's engine, and 1830 when a portable was made by Nathan Gough of Salford. Howden of Boston, another pioneer, reached his twelfth portable on 1839. He then desisted from manufacture fearing that production had outrun demand. In part this decision reveals him to have been a pessimistic and cautious man but again it also reflects how small and precarious the market for portable engines must have been at the time to prompt his reluctance. Two other pioneers who did continue the struggle were Alexander Dean of Birmingham and Ogg of Northampton, followed soon afterwards by Ransomes of Ipswich, and Cambridge of Market Lavington. However, it was not until the middle of the eighteen-forties that there was an appreciable speeding up of the flow of sales of portable engines, and an increase in the number of makers. When it happened it was no sudden release of pent-up potential but rather a quickening of a process already begun. The beneficiaries were not Gough, Howden, Dean, Ogg, or others early on the scene, but, in several cases, newcomers to the market - Tuxford, Clayton & Shuttleworth, and Garrett. The tremendous promotional energy of Nathaniel Clayton (coupled with great personal modesty) and of the third Richard Garrett (far from modest) may explain their success in part, but the technical development of the threshing machine and the sullen acceptance of it by rural labourers after the failure of the 1830 agricultural riots and the crushing out of the trends of unrest they gave expression to were each very important contributors. Not only were threshers growing into reliable machines but farmers at last felt able to introduce them without fear of reprisal. By the time Nathaniel Clayton died in 1883 over 26 000 portables had been made by his firm - many, it is true, for export but a considerable proportion for the home market.

By the eighteen-sixties the use of portables was widespread and commonplace. They were to be found in all manner of employment, often in very incompetent hands and insufficiently maintained. Competition, particularly in the sales of the smaller sizes, was intense, and this, coupled with the absence of experience in the new industry generally, and most acutely in its obscurer practitioners, led to the appearance of much inadequate design and a good deal of poor manufacture. At the 1861 Royal Show the stewards refused to allow one exhibit to be steamed at all. It had only a single stay bolt in each flat plate of its firebox and none in the crown. Of an exhibit at the Smithfield Club Show in 1861 *The Engineer* commented with customary tartness:

> "Smith Bros. of Thrapston sent a diminutive self-propellor, of about the size and cut of a parish fire engine. The boiler had flat sides, the makers having ascertained, we suppose, that square boilers are stronger than round ones. The stay bolts were put in in pairs, each pair being nearly or quite a foot from the nearest pair. A pinion on the engine shaft geared directly into an internal wheel - which might be 1/2 inch or possibly 3/8 inch across its face - this wheel or circular rack being part of the propelling wheel of the engine".

By the early seventies agricultural prosperity was in decline, though not yet routed, but town wages showed a tendency to rise. The attempt by Joseph Arch and his helpers to unionise agricultural workers had been a disastrous failure from their point of view. The resulting upsurge of emigration to towns, to the United States and to the Colonies was a tacit admission that agricultural villages had an excess of population. Farmers alleged that in consequence of this migration agricultural labour had become scarcer and dearer. By 1875 a writer in *Implement & Machinery Review* (anonymous but in all probability the proprietor, Harry Westcott, himself) could write:

> "It is gratifying to know that while the advantages offered in our large towns and colonies have been draining our agricultural districts of their populations and thereby causing labour to be both scarce and dear the land-owner and the agriculturalist have not been left to grapple with the difficulties of their situation unaided. The immense advantages of machinery have been brought under their notice and, as a rule, they have not been slow to avail themselves of it."

The panacea prompting this effusion was a series of vertical boilered portables by Woods, Cocksedge & Company of Stowmarket, Suffolk, one of the minor league of makers so far as portable engine building was concerned. They were not alone in offering small vertical engines on wheels. In 1877 E.S.Hindley of Bourton, Dorset, offered similar machines in sizes from 1 to 5 horsepower, complete with four wheels and horse-shafts, at prices ranging from £42.0.0 for the 1NHP to £117.0.0 for the 5NHP. Farming, however, was descending into depression and by 1880 Cotterell & Co. of Hungerford were offering a somewhat superior series of engines with cross watertube boilers (where Hindley used vertical firetubes), trunk guides and a crankshaft (against Hindley's slide bars and overhung crankpin) at £78.0.0 for a 3NHP and £98.0.0 for a 4NHP - virtually the same price as Hindley's cruder engines three years before, (actually £70.0.0 and £97.0.0 respectively). Many makers offered these small vertical portables and they were used in many trades besides farming. For the makers this was just as well for by the eighties the

Fig.14. The Thomson agricultural steamer Sutherland *built by Ransomes, Sims & Head, and shown at Wolverhampton Royal in 1871. The engine had been turned through 90° compared with* Chenab *(below) so as to allow for the flywheel at the rear.*

Fig.15. (below) Chenab *posed with its omnibus before being shipped to India in 1871.*

Fig.16. Chenab *and its tender in February, 1873, at work between Jhelum and Rawalpindi.*

proliferation of machinery on farms which had seemed set on such a course of expansion three years before had descended in the stagnation that surrounded it for the next fifteen or twenty years.

Philip Pusey, writing in the *Journal of the Royal Agricultural Society of England* (vol.xii p.621) said of portables:

"If a farm be a large one, and especially if, as is often the case, it be of irregular shape, there is a great waste of labour for horses and men in bringing home all the corn in the straw to one point, and in again carrying out the dung to a distance of perhaps two or three miles. It is therefore common, and should be general, to have an outlying yard. This accommodation cannot be reconciled with a fixed engine. If the farm be of a moderate size, it will hardly - and if small will certainly not - bear the expense of a fixed engine: there would be waste of capital in multiplying fixed engines to be worked but a few days in the year. It is now common, therefore, in some counties for a man to invest a small capital in a movable engine, and earn his livelihood by letting it out to the farmer.

But there is a further advantage in these movable engines, little, I believe, if at all, known. Hitherto corn has been thrashed under cover in barns; but with these engines and the improved thrashing-machines we can thrash the rick in the open air at once as it stands. It will be said, How can you thrash out of doors on a wet day? The answer is simple. Neither can you move your rick into a barn on a wet day; and so rapid is the work of the new thrashing-machines, that it takes no more time to thrash the corn than to move it. Open-air thrashing is also far pleasanter and healthier for the labourers, their lungs are not choked with dust, as under cover they are; and there is, of course, a saving of labour to the tenant not inconsiderable. But when these movable steam-engines have spread generally, there will arise an equally important saving to the landlord in buildings. Instead of three or more barns clustering round the homestead, one or other in constant want of repair, a single building will suffice for dressing corn and for chaff-cutting. The very barn floors saved will be no insignificant item. Now that buildings are required for new purposes, we, must, if we can, retrench those buildings whose objects are obsolete. Open-air thrashing may appear visionary, but it is quite common with the new machinery; nor would anyone perform the tedious manoeuvre of setting horses and men to pull down a rick, place it on carts, and build it up again in the barn, who had once tried the simple plan of pitching the sheaves at once into the thrashing machine."

John Wilson and W.T.Thornton, two other prominent pundits of the period, writing in the Encyclopædia Britannica (9th Edition), publicly dissociated themselves from this point of view, advocating fixed engines:

"To us these reasons are inconclusive. A fixed engine can be erected and kept in repair at greatly less cost than a portable one of the same power. It is much easier to keep the steam at working pressure in the common boiler than in the tubular one, which, from its compactness, is generally adopted in portable engines. It is, no doubt, very convenient to draw up engine and machinery alongside a rick and pitch the sheaves at once upon the feeding-board, and very pleasant to do this in the sunshine and "caller air"; but we should think it neither convenient nor pleasant to have thrashing-gear to transport and refix every time of thrashing, to have grain and chaff to cart to the barn, the thrashed straw to convey to the respective places of consumption, and all this in circumstances unfavourable to accurate and cleanly disposal of the products, and excessive exposure to risk of weather. Sudden rain will no doubt interrupt the carrying in of the rick in the one case as the thrashing of it in the other; but there is this vast difference in favour of the former, that the partially carried rick is easily re-covered; machinery, products of thrashing, and work-people, are safely under cover; and the engine is ready by a slight change of gearing for other work, such as bruising, grinding, or chaff-cutting.

It is urged on behalf of the portable engine, that in districts where the farms are generally small, one may serve a good many neighbours. Now, not to dwell on the expense and inconvenience to small occupiers of frequently transporting such heavy carriages, and of having as much of their crop thrashed in a day (there being manifest economy in having at least a day's work when it is employed) as will meet their demands for fodder and litter for weeks to come, we are persuaded that on farms of even 80 or 100 acres, a compact fixed engine of two or three horse-power will thrash, bruise grain, cut chaff, work a churn, and cook cattle food &c. more economically than such work can be done in any other way.

It is very usual to find on such farms, especially in dairy districts, an apparatus for cooking cattle food by steam, or by boiling in a large copper, where as much fuel is used every day, and as much steam generated, as would work such an engine as we have referred to, and do the cooking over and above. Even a small dairy implies a daily demand for boiling water to scrub vessels and cook food for cows. How manifestly economical, then, when the steam is up at any rate, to employ this untiring, obedient agent, so willing to turn the hand of anything, in performing the heavy work of the homestead with a power equal, perhaps, to that of all the men and horses employed upon the farm."

Pusey may not have been entirely right in his advocacy of the portable, for traction engines, after a shaky start, rapidly displaced portables from a number of their avocations, but Wilson and Thornton were totally at variance with the future policy of the farming community in relation to fixed engines. True, many fixed engines already in position continued to serve, in some cases for a long time, whilst their boilers remained serviceable, but the portable and the traction engine soon became the norm.

Relatively to the portable engine the traction engine had been slow in gaining acceptance. Little of note appeared in the eighteen forties until Wilson's 'Farmer's Engine ' of 1849, into which was incorporated gear drive to a sprung axle. It was reported that the engine battered itself to pieces on the roads of the time, but the author's suspicion is that the absence of any arrangement for keeping the gears in truth when

Fig.17. Aveling & Porter's original design of chain-drive traction engine, driven by its builder.

Fig.18. (below) Tuxford's approach to design was rarely fettered by convention, but the road locomotive of 1863 for service between Speyer and Pirmasens (Germany) went to extremes with its double boilers, chimneys, domes and engines. After 77 days it was withdrawn and converted to stationary use.

Fig.19. The Howard Farmer's Engine *owned by James Mason of Eynsford Hall, Oxfordshire, in the yard of the Oxfordshire Steam Ploughing Co. at Cowley.* [Basil Harley]

the axle moved on its springs led to trouble in this part of the design. Despite the interim work of a number of builders in the 1850's it was not until the end of that decade that agricultural traction engines began to be made on a serious scale.

As this book is not a history of the traction engine it is not appropriate to re-examine in detail here the early designs of traction engine, most of which were slanted toward road haulage, the most celebrated being Boydell's and Bray's road locomotives by various makers. Possibly it was felt that the appropriate source of steam power for farm use was the established portable or fixed engine. Apart from Yarrow and Hilditch, none of those who designed, or built, portables or road locomotives had had any connection with the building of steam carriages. The two seemed totally detached from each other. Belief in steam carriages had vanished.

The commercial advent of the agricultural traction engine came mainly through the chain engines of the sixties, the development of which had been triggered by the self-propelling portables of the latter part of the 1850's. Though the myth that Thomas Aveling was the first to make a common portable self-propelling has long been exploded - he had been antedated in this by others including Smith of Coven and Garretts of Leiston - the powerful influence that he had upon the production of a practical traction engine acceptable to the market cannot be denied. Crude though they were in some of their details Aveling's chain engines, made not only in his own works but also by Garretts, Fowlers, and Clayton & Shuttleworth under licence, were an important part of the foundation of the traction engine building trade of this country. This is not to deny the part played by Charles Burrell, who produced a chain driven traction in 1857, but rather to give credit to Aveling for a design which three other makers were pleased to build. Nor must one overlook the fact that having developed and used this design Aveling was soon willing to sacrifice it for one which he thought better, namely the gear driven hornplate traction engine which rapidly became the norm for the agricultural general purpose engine. The most notable of the non-conformist makers were Tuxford of Boston, and James & Frederick Howard of Bedford, both of whom built their own distinctive designs until the eighties.

The characteristic feature in the later Tuxford designs was the reversal of the boiler and driving positions so that the smokebox was at the rear over the driven wheels and the manstand at the front. Howard's idiosyncrasy was to separate the enginework from the boiler by placing it at the rear. The undermounted traction engine, despite its venerable antecedents, acquired no commercial importance in Britain but was extensively used in America, becoming standard for Avery, whilst the three-wheeler, again fairly numerous on other side of the Atlantic, was scarcely more than an aberration here. On the Continent, Albaret, Pécard, and the later German ploughing firms all went for overtypes and four wheels but early on, others, such as Maffei and Cail, went for undertypes. From surviving photographs those of Maffei seem to have resembled Bray's engines.

Vertical boilered traction engines, necessarily involving a separate chassis, were favoured in Europe by Lotz and, later, Bollée, and in America by such firms as Westinghouse, and Daniel Best. Apart from Thomson British designers and makers remained shy of vertical boilers. Alexander Chaplin in Glasgow fitted them mainly because he already used them in steam cranes, of which he was a noted maker. It would, however, have needed only a slight set in the winds of fortune and fashion to have made the Thomson type vertical boilered engine numerically much more prominent than it ever became. Even so its accomplishments were far from negligible. For over fifty years the fleet of Road Steam Engines in Glasgow was dominated by Thomson road steamers. In 1897 Captain Losada, who was manager of the Glasgow Tramways, remarked that in the city "no single article weighing over 10 tons was ever moved except by one of them".

Thomson type road steamers continued to be made until the 1890's, but with a production total of less than a hundred and fifty examples they remained very much in the minority even in their heyday, though they are interesting in more than one aspect, not least in that they formed a link between French, British, and American practice. About the time the first Thomson steamer was built Lotz was running a three-wheeled vertical boilered tractor in Paris, which had characteristics roughly approximating to a Thomson but without Thomson's rubber tyres. Whether or not either copied the other is unknown. Life, in any event, does not go on in a vacuum and many of the individual features of the Thomson, though not the wheels, had been used elsewhere. Thomson engines were exported to the United States and it is

Fig.20. Leonard Todd's four-wheeled bus ran experimentally between Edinburgh and Leith in 1871. This had a Field-tube boiler similar to that in Ravee. The front chimney was the flue, the rear one a ventilator to the saloon.

Fig.21. The 1898 coke-fired bus by David Martyn & Co. of Hebburn-on-Tyne had a boiler described as "horizontal diagonal multi-tubular". This and all machinery was underfloor. The engine contained a good deal of aluminium. In many respects 60 years ahead of its time, it was, nevertheless, a failure.

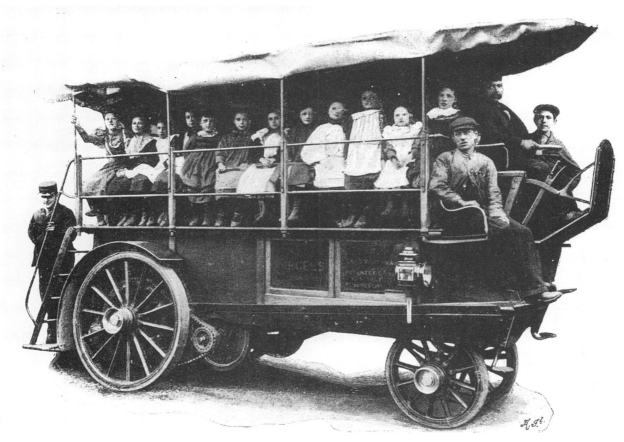

interesting to speculate that the huge three-wheeled engines built by Daniel Best might have developed logically from the Thomsons.

Thomson envisaged his engines being put to use as passenger haulers, Indeed the first engine was exhibited with a trailer omnibus, with which it is reputed to have been exported to Java. Another went to Ceylon, and others to India, as a result of Crompton having, as related, more or less accidentally struck up a correspondence and friendship with Thomson. The Indian examples were used to pioneer the Government road trains, the idea of which Crompton had conceived and had persuaded Lord Mayo into adopting. All these engines suffered from the slowness of Thomson's design of pot-boiler in responding to the fluctuating demands of the engine for steam. In spite of the designer's reluctance to agree to the change Crompton in England in 1870 to commission more rolling stock for the Indian road trains, insisted that boilers with Field tubes ought to be substituted in the four engines he then obtained. Thomson stubbornly resisted this substitution, in the face of which opposition Crompton, stubborn enough himself and not without means, arranged with Lewis Olrick, the London boilermaker, to design and tender for a boiler dimensionally interchangeable with Thomson's but internally of the type he [Crompton] was advocating.

Whilst this argument was going on, mostly by correspondence, the first of the Indian Government engines, *Chenab,* had been completed at Ransomes works in May 1871. Notwithstanding that it was required to run on wood fuel once it had reached India, its boiler made a very poor showing on test in Ipswich, even on good steam coal. Sharpening the blast to increase the draught made it throw out hot cinders and resulted in the burning of the stand at Ipswich race-course, the bill for the repair of which, according to Crompton, had to be met by his principals, the Government of India. The incident heightened Crompton's resolve to insist upon the use of Field tube boilers but *Chenab,* having been entered by its makers for the Royal at Wolverhampton, was sent off there unmodified. Like many Royal Shows in the 1870's, of which Kilburn (1879) was undoubtedly the worst, Wolverhampton suffered from the effects of heavy rain and much wind against which the organisers had made little preparatory provision so that the exhibitors had to endure dire conditions. The second Thomson steamer entered at Wolverhampton, the smaller *Sutherland* (8NHP with horizontal engine) and its crew had a most miserable time. Though the engine did well enough on a metalled road with a gradient of 1 in 20 - 39, hauling three loaded wagons and a portable totalling 26 tons 4 cwt. up the hill with ease, and doing the 1900 feet of the measured course in 10 minutes, she did not do well on turf or the muddy mess into which it was soon churned, for which Thomson's critics blamed the rubber tyres, but the substitution of smooth cast iron wheels for the rubber shod ones in answer to these critics reduced the haulage capacity up the test gradient still more to 13 tons. Naturally this disappointed Thomson but on the other hand when a 10NHP Aveling was tried with the same test load it failed through slipping when only two-thirds of the way up the course. However,*The Engineer,* in reporting the result, appositely commented that the *Sutherland,* with its rubber tyres, cost £750.0.0 whereas the 10NHP Aveling was priced at no more than £390.0.0. The correspondent went on to caution his readers against drawing from this the conclusion that the rubber tyres were valueless but merely, he said, that they had not been able to live up to the extravagant hype given to them in *The Times* and other daily papers, which should have known better. Viewed against the sober expectations of practical men they had done excellently.

On the performance of the pot-boiler of *Chenab* he was much more scathing as well as almost hilariously funny. On the Thursday of the show certain of the engines were tried on a road run of 16 miles to Stafford and back, and *Chenab* joined them as an unofficial entry. It was on this run that an Aveling steam sapper did very well. Thomson had trusted his by now established friend Lieutenant Crompton with the controls. Starting from Wolverhampton just before 7a.m. the party was soon in trouble when it was found that the chimney was too high to go under a railway bridge, a hindrance that took six minutes of time. At Coven, 5 miles from Wolverhampton, a stop was made for water. *The Engineer* recounted:

"The pump was dragged off the top of the omnibus, slid down a board, and planted in an old woman's garden ... The hose was then popped into the old lady's well, without asking her consent. In a minute a good stream was pouring into our tank, and it was not until we had got all the water required that our confiding hostess found that we had pumped her well dry. After this discovery it became expedient that we should proceed as quickly as possible ... and after a slight difference of opinion between Lieut. Crompton and his boiler as to the pressure necessary to drive the *Chenab* had been settled in favour of the former, we started at 7.58. At 8.15 we passed Burrell's locomotive ... and availed ourselves of the opportunity to extinguish the lagging of *Chenab's* boiler, which had taken fire at the smokebox. Thomson's pot-boiler is the best I ever saw for burning off lagging ... I may add here that the way in which Lieut. Crompton took his engine over heaps of stones by the roadside and into complicated holes and trenches when passing other engines was sufficient to startle weak nerves. I began to think that the *Chenab* had been designed *pour la chasse.*"

At Penkridge, the second water stop, Crompton had problems again:

"There was a serious difficulty, indeed, between Lieut. Crompton and the boiler, which very nearly ended in victory for the latter. The boiler would have it that 50lb. pressure was all that was needed, Lieut, Crompton insisted on 75lb. as a minimum. The contention was very sharp, but ended in the defeat of the boiler for the time."

Notwithstanding this derision it should be remembered that despite these set-backs *Chenab* made the 16 mile journey in two and a half hours. Not having been entered it did not receive any formal accolade. This went to the other Thomson engine *Sutherland* which made the time of 3 hours 35 minutes the best time of any of the official entries.

In the stop-over period at Stafford Crompton took steps to deal with some at least of the boiler problems of *Chenab*. The man from *The Engineer* rejoined the party for the return trip. He found that Lieut. Crompton had:

"treated his boiler to a dose of red lead and oatmeal to stop a leak or leaks - let me say leaks. How the matter had been adjusted between the Lieutenant and his boiler I cannot pretend to say, but we had a fair pressure of steam on starting at 6p.m., or thereabouts, and rattled along at a good pace along the wrong road: we smashed through boughs, and traversed paths unknown to the tire of india-rubber, for more than an hour ... The mode of procedure was this: first we got up steam, and ran until it fell down again; then we stopped and pumped up the boiler; then we got up steam again as high as the boiler would let us: then we started and ran a little way, and repeated these operations over and over until we reached Four Ashes. Here the difficulty I have already alluded to as existing between Lieut. Crompton and his boiler assumed very serious proportions. Early in the day he had blown the spark catcher out of the chimney: now, here at Five Ashes, more than five miles from home, he discovered he had melted off the copper nozzle of his blowpipe. A contest now commenced between the boiler and everybody as to whether it would or would not make steam. In the end everybody was beaten, Lieut. Crompton went to bed in the Omnibus, his men went to bed on the Omnibus. Under the circumstances I thought I would walk on. I did so, and reached Wolverhampton after a walk of four or five miles, which I did not want, over a very pretty road which I did not want to see; I amused myself en route by composing complimentary phrases concerning the *Chenab* and the pot-boiler."

The upshot of this trip was the total reinforcement of Crompton's conviction that a change of boiler was required. Despite the troubles at Wolverhampton Thomson still was not convinced that the pot-boiler had to be replaced by Olrick's boiler with the Field tubes. The opportunity of providing proof by a typical Cromptonian gesture shortly presented itself when the sister-engine, *Ravee*, with its Olrick-designed boiler, reached completion at Ipswich. With his characteristic boldness, not to say brashness, Crompton resolved to drive the newly completed steamer from Ipswich to Edinburgh to show Thomson how it performed. It had already given a good account of itself on trial at Ipswich. Whereas the pot-boiler of *Chenab*, supposedly designed for wood fuel, had failed to keep steam even on coal, the Field tube boiler of *Ravee* steamed well on wood and had to have its grate area reduced with firebrick to enable it to be fired on coal. The full grate area was 11.25 square feet but experience determined that with good coal an area of 7.6 square feet was ample. Besides the driver and fireman Crompton had a fitter with him on this remarkable trip. Crompton, himself only twenty-six, noted in his journal of the trip that the driver was only seventeen years old, but he performed admirably. The four intrepid young men set off from Ransomes, Sims & Head's works at 3.40a.m. on September 28, 1871. The early start (4.40a.m. at today's reckoning under British Summer Time) was presumably to allow them to clear the the town without too many eyes being upon them. Crompton was not a retiring man but he had already endured much sarcasm from *The Engineer* over the trip from Wolverhampton to Stafford so he probably preferred no publicity at all to the possibility of another roasting.

By 6.15a.m. on the first day *Ravee* and the omnibus reached Ely having encountered no especial obstacles beyond the fact that the road was mostly deep in dust and abounding in loose flints. Water shortage, the bane of railway steam locomotive men in East Anglian summers, also affected Crompton's party, particularly at Stowmarket, where they could obtain no more than 259 gallons, and at Newmarket, where the only water they could get was in a tank in the back yard of a public house accessible only with buckets. To quote from Crompton's account:

"We coaled at Ely, and got a guide for Peterborough - such a designing ruffian! His sole mission appeared to be to guide us into scrapes. Our troubles commenced about ten miles after leaving Ely. Our guide piloted us into a cul de sac, terminating in a triangular piece of ground, as boggy and treacherous as you please. As its greatest diameter was about 30ft. it required some manoeuvring to twist the train round and come out again. A few miles on we crossed a very indifferent wooden bridge. The wooden bridges in the Fens are most of them built on this plan: the piers are of piles, and the roadway is laid on 14 in. square oak baulks, untrussed in any way. When the spans are short this is all very well, but when they get to 18 ft. and 20 ft. as is the case with some of the bridges near Peterborough, traction engines had better go round. However, Meeple Bridge was judged to be safe. Shortly after crossing it, and a second one over the Forty Foot river, our guide insisted upon our turning sharp round to the left, and taking the road along the top of the bank of the Forty Foot. This road was tolerably wide at first, but gradually narrowed until it was only about 10ft. at the top, with a steep slope on one side to the river, on the other to the Fen ditch. The surface consisted of a thin coating of metal laid on the springy Fen soil of the bank, and the whole rose and fell under the engine like the waves of the sea. It was an anxious time for the steersman, as he had only a margin of a few inches outside each driving wheel, and if he came within this margin ever so little the side of the bank immediately began to cut and slide away under the wheel. We had ten miles of this fearful road, but to the honour of the rubber tire, be it said, it never once failed us in a situation where a slip or failure to bite for one single instant would have been a very serious matter."

Feeding the boiler with water from the Forty Foot river led to priming but the final trouble was the parting of a defective fire-weld in one of the Field tubes which put out the fire. As it was then 2a.m. on Saturday morning and over twenty hours had elapsed since their start from Ipswich of which twelve hours and nine minutes had been spent actually travelling the 69 miles they had covered, they can be excused for resting whilst the boiler cooled.

In the morning they knocked out and replaced the split tube, filled the boiler, raised steam and set off again at 12.30p.m. Twelve miles further on they at last reached the Great North Road at Sawtry. After taking off the chain armour from the wheels they ran the next seventeen miles to Wansford in less than two hours. There they remained during Sunday as guests at Stibbington House. The next day they were away at 6a.m. for Doncaster, 83½ miles on, which they reached at 11.30p.m. The running time was 10 hours 25 minutes and the average speed almost eight miles per hour, but this disappointed Crompton who expostulated "we should easily have averaged twelve miles per hour, but for the frequent stoppages for horses, the slow speeds through villages, etc." This may have been so but bowling along the Great North Road, even at the speed he complained of, without the chain armour on the tyres had caused the tyre on the single leading wheel to develop serious signs of distress. The next day, after 42 miles, the travellers had to pull off the road at Boroughbridge to remove the mangled remains of the tyre and to improvise a repair of wooden felloes and iron tyre bands. The result enabled them to travel at speeds not above about 5mph. at which travelling became fearfully uncomfortable. They concluded the day's travel at Azerley Hall where they waited for eight days, firstly for the arrival of a new rubber tyre, and then the ceasing of the drenching rain which had enveloped the expedition. By October 2 it was still raining and the party could wait no longer. Perhaps, indeed, they had overstretched the hospitality of Azerley Hall. In the wet, therefore, they made a relatively late start at 8a.m. and travelled to Darlington. Misfortune hit them again the next day when they bent a connecting rod and spent seven hours straightening and refitting it at Ferryhill.

Crompton refused to be delayed and after having got to Durham at 9p.m. they continued on to Newcastle where they arrived at the High Level Bridge at 3.10 the following morning. Officialdom barred it to them and so they had to turn round and go over the Low Level Bridge. *Ravee* managed the climb up from the Low Level Bridge, 1 in 13, at 6mph. and soon they were on the road to Morpeth pausing for coal at Seaton Burn Colliery. A mid-morning breakfast at Morpeth prepared them for the bleak passage of the undulating moorland road to Wooler, a constant succession of long and steep grades. Near Wooler they were denied passage of a toll gate but by taking off the headlamp and easing the engine up to the gate they opened it without trouble or damage. When they came to rest in Wooler they had been in motion for 19¼ hours plus another 20¼ hours spent in repairs, coaling and watering and occasionally, to allow the crew to rest and eat. Throughout this period of 39½ hours it had never ceased to rain and the roads were muddy and heavy. The same conditions prevailed on the remaining 70 miles to Edinburgh. Lootry Hill, 3½ miles long graded from 1 in 25 to 1 in 17, was taken in triumph and was breasted with the water level maintained in the glass and a good head of steam.

The steamer remained in Edinburgh for close on three weeks which were, no doubt, a welcome opportunity for the crew to catch up on sleep. Thomson was able to see the engine in action and Crompton, doubtless, impressed upon him the advantages of Olrick's boiler design. With particular bearing upon its future role in India it was demonstrated before Thomas Monteath, Director-General of the Indian Post Office whose family home was at Lockerbie. Its triumph was to haul 26½ tons up a mile of 1 in 17. In deference to the interest of the Indian Government in the journey of *Ravee* from Ipswich to Edinburgh and back it had been accorded the status of service of the Crown. In consequence the restrictions of the Locomotive Acts did not have any power over the crew and Crompton had made good use of this freedom on his way north on the Great North Road, at one point racing a Great Northern Railways goods train where road and rail parallelled, at speeds in excess of 25mph.

Fig.22. By the end of the last century the traction engine outnumbered all other steam road vehicles. Here a 7NHP Allchin single is threshing on the farm of E.L.Dwight at Berkhamsted, Herts.

Fig.23. The portable, of all ages and many sizes, remained popular, and the example in the picture was pumping water for hop-spraying about the turn of the century, near Tonbridge, Kent.

The arrival of *Ravee* and its bus in Edinburgh culminated a year that had seen three other steam buses demonstrated there. All had been designed and built locally, a fact which, taken with Thomson being domiciled in Edinburgh, made that city a hot bed of ideas on steam vehicle development. Nairn of Leith, who had already built a tractor on Thomson's principles, had also made a three-wheeled self-contained double decker design with a horizontal flue running along the upper deck and discharging at the rear. Todd, also of Leith, had built a 50-seater double decker, again on three wheels, which put in four months of service on the Edinburgh to Portobello route in the summer of 1871 with variable success. He followed this with a design for a four-wheeler which was built but probably never ran in revenue earning service. The third bus to run in Edinburgh was that constructed by Todd on a four-wheeled chassis with a double decked body not dissimilar to that used on Nairn's bus but distinguishable by the vertical chimney and the matching ventilating trunking from the enclosed saloon. Like Gurney, Nairn used direct drive but Todd, no doubt with a mind to the problem of springing, used a counter shaft and coupling rod drive.

None of these three interesting ventures into steam passenger transport came to anything permanently. Even in the Punjab Crompton was forced by Government parsimony of funds to make do with a motley collection of vehicles for his road trains which continued to run until he was recalled to his regiment in 1875 whereupon, notwithstanding this promising and extended trial, the whole project was superseded by metre gauge railways. Militarily this was probably right as the railways, once built, enabled troops and their equipment to be moved relatively quickly from place to place but for the needs of the local civil population the road trains would have been just as satisfactory at a fraction of the cost of the railways. In the early seventies, however, British India still lived in the shadow of the Mutiny which probably weighed heavily in favour of the railways and their military capabilities. In Edinburgh the coming of cable trams cut away the ground from under the feet of Todd and Nairn. They were helped by operational shortcomings of the vehicles themselves, and the propensity of Todd's three-wheeler for turning over, but the underlying problem was the level of restriction on speed and movement imposed by the Locomotive Acts of 1865 and 1868. What is of some interest is that when the building of steam buses was resumed after the emancipation of 1896 a considerable superficial family likeness was discernible between the buses then built and the Todd four-wheeler, very noticeable in the David Martyn bus of 1896 but still observable even in Clarkson vehicles of a decade later.

Thomson, undoubtedly the foremost of the Edinburgh trio, was stricken with locomotor ataxia. When Crompton met him in 1870 his life was divided between bed, couch, and wheelchair. On March 8, 1873, he died at the early age of fifty-one, and with his death the impelling force behind the road steamers was extinguished. Had his physical decline and early death not supervened possibly they might have made more headway against the Aveling type traction engine. In the event they languished after he was removed from the scene, their decline assisted by the uncompromising opposition of the *ad hoc* bodies concerned with road traffic to all mechanical traction on the road, and by the general antipathy of vested interests to steam traction on the roads.

Chapter 2

Steam as a Rival

That prop of Christmas card illustrators, the stage-coach, which sprang into being, flourished, and perished in little more than a hundred years (say 1750-1850) employed upward of 100 000 horses at its peak. Nevertheless it was but a small sector of the horse economy as a whole. It is estimated that in 1811 the horse population of Great Britain was of the order of 1 287 000. By 1901 it was some 3 250 000 of which London alone employed 100 000 heavy draught-horses and 250 000 other sorts.

A heavy horse produced about 20lb. of ordure daily, and about 5 gallons of urine, part of which it was thoughtful enough to deposit in its stable but probably half of which it left in the streets and thoroughfares in which it worked. London in the second half of the last century was comparatively well organised to deal with such leavings. The principal streets were staffed with boy street orderlies whose function it was to remove horse dung as it fell using high sided shovels and short brooms, depositing what they gathered in fixed kerbside or island bins from which it was later removed in carts. The boys on these duties, about 200 in the City of London alone, darted about amongst the traffic in apparent hazard of their lives in a never ceasing battle to control the accumulation of excrement. An admiring American, George Soper, commented in 1909; "The agility and skill of these boys are remarkable. Using a scoop resembling a short-handled shovel with an inverted handle and a short broom a boy can pick up the fresh droppings of a horse in less than ten seconds." At recognised points a crossing sweeper kept a path swept so that pedestrians might cross the carriage way. Some sweepers were paid by the local authority, others were freelances existing on tips. Without them crossing the street would have been a hazardous matter, especially for women in long skirts.

In the best class of streets the carriage ways were flushed by hoses from hydrants at night but outside the West End and City not much was done. Asphalt and sett roads were easy to clean but wood-block paving, of which there was a good deal, and particularly in Westminster, because of its deadening effect upon the sound of iron-tyred vehicles, was absorbent and soaked up horse urine with the result that in warmer weather the atmosphere in such streets had a heavily ammoniacal overlay. Where a road was paved with water-bound macadam there were the added problems of dust in dry weather and mud when it was wet. Scraping of such roads by a wooden scraper or peel was practised to remove the deposits of mud and ordure wherever funds permitted but mostly they did not and the surfaces retained their coating of mixed filth.

Arthur Lenton (step-father of the author's mother) lived in Clapham, South London, in the days of horse buses and horse trams. Beyond an occasional traction engine mechanical transport was never seen in the streets. Large industrial refrigeration plants had arrived on the scene but not on a scale small enough to reach into the shops of Clapham. Fishmongers and some butchers bought ice from such suppliers as Carlo Gatti, or Stevensons, but fish shops in particular tended to smell high. In summer the streets reeked. The poor lived in small, often overcrowded houses with a water tap over the sink, or in the court outside. Bathrooms, indeed, were not common even in the houses of the better-off. A man who bathed once a week was thought to be tolerably fastidious and it was expected that most people would have a certain amount of personal odour whilst many frankly stank. Men's suits were largely of wool-based cloth which could not be washed, whilst dry-cleaning existed only on a limited scale, and even where it was available it was beyond the means of most poorer people. Consequently much clothing went uncleaned from the time it was new until it wore out.

This striving, steaming, stinking mass of activity was served by horse traffic that had vast ramifications and created an enormous vested interest. Aside from the obvious interests of carters, mates, ostlers, shoeing-smiths, horse-dealers, horse-slaughterers (for there were numerous casualties, and the works of John Harrison & Sons of Belle Isle, London, alone processed the carcases of 10 000 horses annually), horse doctors, singers (who singed, not sang), harness makers, and provender dealers, there were tentacles of interest stretching far back. Hay and straw came to London by whole trains of road wagons, mostly at night. The owners and crews of stackie barges obtained a living by barging the same commodities from the rivers and creeks of East Anglia to the Metropolis. Horse transport and the railways had by then reached equilibrium and the cartage of horse-feed had become an appreciable and valued traffic on the railways also.

In the reverse direction train-loads of stable manure left London daily for country destinations, providing a major source of humus and nitrogen. As early as 1865 it was reported that one farm of 445 acres at Wheathampstead, Hertfordshire, received by rail 1 000 tons of horse dung a year taken by contract from a 200 horse stable. Another of 620 acres near East Ham, given over to market gardening, took 10 000 tons a year. The delivered price at Wheathampstead was 6s.6d. a ton. Much was consigned to Kent also for the hop farms of the Weald. In the country-side itself the growing of horse feed - hay, oats, beans, and carrots - was an important side of agricultural activity more so as wheat for bread-making imported from the Americas and Australia, entering tariff free, undercut the home product.

The value of this commerce of the horse was enormous. W.J.Gordon in *The Horseworld of London* (1893) calculated that a horse in heavy work such as a bus horse or a horse on dock or railway cartage cost about 10s.0d. a week to feed and bed, though tradesmen's and cabmen's horses cost rather less, and costers' ponies much less. Taking the London horse population as between 350 000 and 375 000, and the average feeding cost as 7s.6d. a week this equated to an annual bill in excess of £6 000 000 at a time when the total value of agricultural production was about £200 million. [From E.M.Ojala *Agriculture & Economic Progress* (1982). Dr.Collins of Institute of Agricultural History considers £205 million closer.] Shoeing, another considerable expense with horses, cost about £20.0.0 a year for a bus horse or heavy cart horse, so it is probable, though no statistics exist, that shoeing smiths might have enjoyed a total income of over £4 million a year. All this added up to a vast, though uncoordinated, vested interest directed against efforts to supersede the horse by mechanical traction.

If, in towns and cities, mechanical road traction faced massive opposition, active and passive, there was probably an intenser, even if numerically smaller, antipathy to it in the countryside. English farming had undergone a radical transformation in the hundred years between 1735 and 1835 which had seen the inclosure of commons and the disappearance of the common field system. Notwithstanding this the customs and practices of the stable were very set and the lore of the farm horsemen had roots traceable to the Middle Ages. Of the even older form of draught, oxen, there still remained a body of adherents, and indeed the practice of working oxen continued in Gloucestershire until 1945. In the hierarchy of a large farm the order of precedence among the horsemen was carefully guarded. To be head horseman was a sought-after position, the incumbent of which was at pains to prevent any usurping of his status. A predominantly arable farm of 600 acres probably gave employment to 24 horses and four horsemen with help from day-men, and to be head of this establishment conferred an importance probably not excelled by any other workman on the farm.

The arrival of threshing machines on farms in the first two or three decades of the nineteenth century had caused great resentment amongst the day-labourers to whom the drudgery of threshing by flail in the winter months had presented an alternative to penury. A few early threshers, such as that on the Trewithen estate of Sir Christopher Hawkins as noted in Chapter 1, were steam powered, and a few were driven by water wheels, but most had horse-powers to provide the drive so that, if anything, they augmented the work for the stable and in so doing avoided conflict with the horse community.

The spread of portables in the 1840's and 50's, and the subsequent influx of traction engines had been quite a different proposition since not only had they displaced horses but also had introduced a grade of workman not conformable to the unwritten but nevertheless real code of gradation in the farm establishment. Ploughing by steam made the matter worse by a direct and important encroachment upon the preserves of the horse and of the surviving yokes of oxen. The steam ploughmen were a positive affront, better paid, independent, and heedless of horse traditions or of those whose preserves they trampled upon. To make matters worse they required menial attendance by the horses in hauling coal and water to the field. Before the necessary and painful adjustments which these changes of circumstance occasioned had taken place fully, agriculture in Great Britain suffered the reversal of fortune embodied in the agricultural depression, at its worst from the awful summer of 1879 to about the late nineties. All suffered from it - horse ploughmen as well as steam ploughmen - but possibly the latter had the worst of it. There was over provision of equipment, a circumstance destined to recur in the aftermath of the first world war, in both steam ploughing and steam rolling, and acreage rates were consequently cut to skeleton figures by the resulting competition for what work there was.

There are no statistics available of total engine population during this period, but the table below gives the figures for sales in Kent, a county giving a good spread of land use, varying from rich arable in the East and North East; through high downland in the North and South East; drained marshes in the South; large mixed farms, with fruit and hops, in the Weald; to greater emphasis on stock on the Sussex (and to a lesser extent, Surrey) borderland.

Table 1

Sales of agricultural (both traction and ploughing) engines in Kent up to 1899

N.B. A total of 71 engines had been delivered prior to 1870.

YEAR	No.	YEAR	No.	YEAR	No.
1870	18	1880	11	1890	15
1871	32	1881	10	1891	8
1872	20	1882	15	1892	10
1873	8	1883	14	1893	9
1874	11	1884	16	1894	7
1875	17	1885	10	1895	4
1876	20	1886	13	1896	11
1877	26	1887	6	1897	5
1878	13	1888	11	1898	8
1879	18	1889	9	1899	15
Decade total	183		115		92
			= 62.84% of 1870/79		= 50.27% of 1870/79

Figures compiled by Mr. W.S.Love

The figures show how the increase in the rate of use of steam power in agriculture, which in the seventies seemed to be rising, underwent a reversal in the eighties and nineties. During that period, in fact, steam power and horse power on farms had attained an uneasy equilibrium, which still obtained in the furthest stretches of contemporary living memory.

During the nineties, the period of Arthur Lenton's recollections of urban Clapham, a far from prosperous agricultural and farming community in rural areas looked to the horse economy of towns and cities for an important part of its trade - not only horse feed and bedding but also the breeding, breaking-in, and training of horses. If townspeople had cause to fear the changes that the substitution of mechanical for horse traction was to bring about how much more had the country-side good reason to view the prospect with trepidation. A horse-bus driver might not have relished the idea of having to learn to manage a steam or petrol engined bus but at least it was a matter only of distaste for change. A discerning farm worker of that time, on the other hand, contemplating the future course of events would have faced a prospect in which a considerable percentage of farming would no longer have a market. How high a percentage this actually was is not capable of being simply stated. It has been estimated by F.M.L.Thompson that the total value of feeding stuffs (but not bedding) consumed by urban horses in 1900 was of the order of £18 640 000, representing about 1 540 000 tons of oats, beans, and grains, and 2 640 000 tons of hay, or about 12% of the total production of these items. Though the estimation of these figures involved their author in problems of delineation and of definition they are valuable as a measure of what British agriculture might have expected to forego in the event of the horse giving place to the machine.

This, then, is also the measure of the vested interest that had to be disarmed or won over before machines could make worthwhile headway over horses on the streets. By the mid-nineties street tramways, on which the limited use of steam had not been an unqualified success, were already making use of electric traction which was poised to sweep away the tram horse in little more than a decade. This is a subject outside our present scope, but the first five years of the nineties saw an appreciable change also in attitudes to other forms of road traction which do have a direct bearing on our subject.

The middle years of the last century had seen *ad hoc* authority in local government at its peak. The frightful urban inheritance of the industrial revolution from, say, about 1760 onward had presented the social conscience of Victorian England with the problems of large inchoate areas of town development unprovided with the most elementary amenities, unsewered, unpaved, and provided with no fit water supplies or burial grounds. The first important step on the path of reform was the Municipal Corporations Act 1835 which remodelled existing boroughs and created new ones in areas deemed to be of appropriate size and importance, providing both sorts with borough councils elected on a limited franchise. In the case of the smaller towns, most were designated Improvement Act Districts under Improvement

Fig.24. *Aveling & Porter 15-ton roller No.500 (February 29,1872) supplied to the London master paviours Mowlem, Freeman & Co.*

Fig.25. *One of the limited number of rollers, all equipped with vertical boilers, built by Alexander Chaplin & Co. in Glasgow. The example shown had 6 in. x 13 in. double cylinders placed vertically immediately behind the boiler.*

Commissioners. In addition there were created school boards, highway boards, burial boards, boards of guardians (for the administration of the poor law), and boards for lighting and watching, most of them charged with the care of districts whose boundaries were coterminous neither with each other nor with county, borough, or improvement district boundaries.

The work of these improving authorities in tackling the roads and streets under their control provided the market for the early Aveling Batho rollers either by direct purchase or through the contracting firms who carried out street works. Of the first fifteen rollers supplied by Aveling & Porter ten went direct to road authorities - at Liverpool; Sheffield; Maidstone; Islington; Leeds; Darlington; St.George's, Hanover Square, London; and Hull, whilst the remainder went to contractors as in the case of No.500 which was owned by Mowlem, Freeman & Co., the prominent London street contractors, whose successors are still in business. Boroughs outside London had their powers consolidated and augmented by the Municipal Corporations Act 1882 which made them the road authorities for all roads within their boundaries other than 'main roads' (mostly the former turnpikes) which remained the responsibility of the counties, but even this limitation was removed in respect of some of the major boroughs by the Local Government Act of 1888 which both set up county councils and conferred upon the new class of 'county boroughs' the same powers as those exercised by a county council. In London, despite the creation of the London County Council in 1888, responsibility for roads remained in the hands of vestries until the creation of the Metropolitan Boroughs under the London Government Act of 1899. Despite the archaic origin of their powers under which they were made responsible for road management the London vestries had adopted progressive policies toward steam rolling. Besides the vestries of Islington, and St. George's, those of Paddington, St. Marylebone, and Kensington were also early users of Aveling's rollers. Curiously though it was not the principal streets and thoroughfares which required the services of a steam roller as these were paved, in the main, with surfaces laid by hand - setts, wood blocks, or asphalt - but rather the lesser and peripheral roads laid with water bound macadam.

During the sixties and seventies Aveling & Porter had virtually a monopoly of what market there was for rollers. Thomas Green & Sons of Leeds took a limited part during the eighties, predominantly in the North, but it was not until after the administrative reforms of the late eighties, coupled with the demands of the Road Improvements Association, initiated not so much by motorists as by the growing army of cyclists, that other major makers were tempted into the market by the prospect of a much greater demand for rollers. The arrival on the scene of non-horse traffic in considerable volume and the voting powers of its owners and users were the stimuli that caused the changes of attitude in both central and local government politicians.

In the early nineties only the emergence of the electric tram was seen as potentially menacing by the railway companies. Steam or motor buses had scarcely yet appeared, and steam haulage of goods was too slow to seem to imperil rail traffic. Indeed the use of mechanical road traction, insofar as it was considered at all by railway senior management from the exalted dais on which it sat, was looked upon as a possible improver of feeder services.

Poor communications were viewed, with good reason, as important contributors to the general malaise of farming. The building of rural branch railways had, however, involved most of the promoters, whether local people or main line railway companies, in financial loss and the then fashionable panacea was the building of light railways, of either standard or narrow gauge, to standards of engineering and equipment more relaxed than those called for by the general legislation governing the construction and use of main line railways. In return onerous restrictions were placed upon speed. The Light Railways Act was passed in 1896, the same year as the Locomotives on Highways Act which emancipated the motor car and opened the way for steam tractors and wagons. The Bill for the latter was introduced in the House of Commons by Henry Chaplin, President of the Local Government Board. Speculating about the future he remarked that the Bill would "undoubtedly develop a very great and, having regard to their experience with bicycles, quite possibly an enormous trade and give a vast amount of employment". His words were greeted with "Hear, hear". As he continued that "it was even possible that these motor cars might become a rival to light railways" he was greeted with laughter. Few believed that mechanisation on the road could either displace the horse or usurp the position of the railway. All these scoffers were to be proved wrong but it was to be the horse on which the first brunt fell. Within ten years of the passing of the Locomotives on Highways Act steam and motor tractors and lorries had become an established branch of manufacture, component makers had sprung up, sales of accessories were being canvassed, and a trade press flourished. By the passage of twenty years after the Act the bus horse had become a creature all but extinct, and large inroads had been made into the preserves of the heavy draught horse.

The revolution did not go unchallenged, and the local government establishment fought a determined rearguard action. Magistrates, whether Justices of the Peace or Stipendaries, on the whole viewed mechanical traffic on the road with disfavour, and convicted owners and drivers for trifling offences and on dubious evidence. Dick Frampton was on Mann's wagon No.1120, owned by his brother Tom of Farnham, Surrey, when it was timed by the police at Honiton passing over a measured ¼ mile at 12½mph. when the legally permitted speed was only 12mph. A conviction followed.

It has been stated that in 1909 one Bench imposed fines totalling £1 000 on motor drivers in a single week (probably about £230 000 in 1993 money values). On the whole magistrates did not give motoring offenders the benefit of the doubt. Indeed, it was suggested that, since most of them were councillors or ratepayers, they had a vested interest in securing the maximum income from fines as until the Road Act 1920 the proceeds of such fines went into local Police Funds. There was, of course, much that deserved to be viewed with disfavour. There were no legal requirements as to ability to drive, and the purchase of a 5s.0d. driving licence was the only prerequisite to mounting a vehicle, however potentially lethal, and driving it. Many of the new owners and drivers were not only ignorant of how to drive properly but had, besides, only the haziest ideas of what was required by way of maintenance, and consequently the shortcomings in design which occurred as designers and makers felt their way were compounded by lack of knowledge in those charged with the task of keeping the vehicles in repair.

Nevertheless, despite many owners and drivers thus courting retribution, it was a fact that certain areas of the country had become notorious for capricious policing and the severity of their magisterial benches. Of the Home Counties, Surrey, and East and West Sussex were particularly singled out. They were not alone, for in Northumberland the proportion of convictions to prosecutions in motoring offences rose from 51% in 1906 to 79% in 1908 and an incredible 83% in 1909. The extent of police caprice in bringing prosecutions was illustrated by a memorandum to the Home Office from a Hampshire Bench of more temperate views, complaining that the local Police insisted on bringing daily an extended list of charges against motorists - as many as 80 per day and sometimes more - on trifling technical matters such as the numbers on registration plates being larger or smaller by insignificant amounts than the regulations laid down. Mostly the magistrates dismissed the charges in such instances, but the Police persisted in bringing them. Conditions were not, of course, constant over the whole country. Most friction occurred, as one would have expected, in areas where mechanised road traffic was at its maximum, the 'stock-broker belt' in Surrey and Sussex for private motoring, and the industrial areas of the Midlands and North, particularly the Lancashire cotton area, for industrial traffic. Parts of England, such as the Fens, much of Central and Border Wales, and the so-called crofter counties of Scotland remained deeply rural and not much frequented by either private or commercial motors whether steam or internal combustion.

Aside from opposition to mechanical traction arising from vested interest the fury heaped upon the machine arose mainly from two matters, namely the unacceptable level of death and injury to road users, brought about chiefly by the faster private motor car or by motor buses, and the nuisance caused by road dust in areas outside large towns. Again most steam commercials were too slow to raise the dust in any degree and it was buses, charabancs, and private cars which were the main offenders. The point held most against the steam vehicle, however, was its propensity for scaring horses.

In the period 1896-1906 farming was just beginning to pick itself up from the level to which it had fallen during the worst of the agricultural depression. Fruit and vegetable growing in the areas with ready access to London provided one of the ways to recovery. Rural production of fresh milk was another, and dust damage was inimical to the expansion of both but particularly to fruit. London was still sufficiently limited in extent for the Express Dairy Co.Ltd. to be able to have dairy farms at Finchley only 9 miles from Charing Cross but milk production for use in towns was in fact spreading out along the main lines of railway which provided transport to the Metropolis. Milk was to be a life-line for farmers along the Thames Valley and in South West England forced out of grain growing by imports from America.

As in other major changes in farming patterns the way was led, or at least the paths forward explored, by the somewhat disparaged race of 'gentlemen farmers' and by the owners of large estates, frequently men who had earned fortunes in other pursuits some part of which they were prepared to spend in model farming or agricultural experiment. In politics the Liberals were entirely wedded to free trade whilst the Conservatives were protectionists only to a slight degree. Consequently virtually a free market economy prevailed in all fields germane to this narrative, with the result that the ordinary farmer was so constrained financially as to be simply unable to fund consistent or prolonged experiments out of the revenues available to him, or to undertake the hazards of wholesale innovation even if impelled, as relatively few were, by intellectual or economic curiosity or by a sense of public duty to undertake research. Many of the innovators of the fifties, sixties, and seventies, the formative years of the use of steam on the land or in rural industries, had been either themselves drawn from the ranks of those with means independent of their farming or were sponsored by men so liberated from the financial restraints of the ordinary farmer.

Sometimes such sponsors had been members of the traditional and aristocratic landowning families. Possibly the most celebrated of these was George Leveson-Gower, the third Duke of Sutherland, of Dunrobin Castle, Sutherland, who has already been noted in Chapter 1 as the owner of a Rickett-built steam carriage. His objective in agricultural improvement had been to better the lot of his small farmer tenants by providing them with the means of growing turnips and other winter feed stuffs for stock, which at that time were having to be brought in each winter from outside the area covered by his estates. The Duke had been in Egypt during the cotton boom, occasioned by the American Civil War, when ploughing sets had been used with marked success in the Nile Delta. He was thus inspired to seek the advice of David Greig of Fowlers. In 1871, with Fowler 's engines and tackle, fifty acres of moorland at Uppat, near Brora, were cleared of rock, broken to the plough, drained, limed and manured, forming at the conclusion of the work good class arable land but, unfortunately at a price of £50 per acre whereas at the outset the cost had been estimated at £18.10.0 an acre. The knack of over-running the estimate obviously did not begin with the Humber Bridge.

Undefeated, the Duke himself and John McLennan, manager of his farms, designed implements of dimensions massive enough to cope with the conditions encountered. The Duke designed a steel framed cultivator with a large single tine each end, capable of entering thirty inches into the soil, and by its passage dislodging rocks and roots, which were then cleared from the surface by a scoop developed by Max Eyth of Fowlers. The stone thus recovered was used for roads, for lining boundary dykes, and for forming French drains over drain tiles. The drain tiles were also a product of the estate, being made at Brora, and the fuel for firing them came from the Duke's mine there. McLennan designed a massive breaking plough for the first ploughing of the cleared land. By 1874 some 2 000 acres had been cleared near Loch Shin, followed by further work in Strath Kildonan, so that by 1878 about 28 000 acres had been reclaimed in all. By the time this huge effort had come to an end the Duke owned sixteen Fowler ploughing engines, seven traction engines by the same maker, and six of other makes. It must be recorded with regret that the culmination of this herculean task of reclamation coincided with the onset of the agricultural depression so that neither the Duke nor his tenants received the expected rewards.

Not all innovators had worked on this scale nor had commanded means of this order. Usher, for instance, who had experimented exhaustively with a self-propelled steam ploughing engine carrying the implement on its own frame was an Edinburgh brewer and though comfortably off was not in possession of the financial resources available to the Duke of Sutherland. Though he was unable to translate his ideas into workable practice at the time, he was vindicated eighty years later by the practical, if not financial, workability of the Fowler Gyrotiller (1932) and by the tractor mounted implement systems of Harry Ferguson (1933 and on). Perhaps the best known of the mid-Victorian improvers was J.J.Mecchi of Kelvedon, Essex, a London Italian barber, who made a fortune from his invention of a patent razor strop and spent nearly all of it on experiments in agriculture on his Essex estate. Mecchi spent money on many things other than machinery but he is notable for having helped to finance the Romaine steam-diggers which, like all other efforts in the same field, ultimately came to nothing.

Despite this, the lengthy development of steam diggers by Darby, Cooper, and Procter continued well into this century but, notwithstanding the devotion of their designers and the investment of large sums of money in their production, steam diggers never achieved real or sustained financial success. Colin Tyler has looked at length into the reasons why this should have been so and therefore there is no good purpose to be served by reiterating his conclusions here, but it is perhaps pertinent to remark that in their basic principle of using a tractor mounted power source they, like Usher, were early in the field with what later was to become a widely applied practice.

Table 2
Arable Land Acreage in Great Britain

Year	England and Wales	Scotland	Great Britain
1866	14,266	3,265	17,531
1867	14,433	3,326	17,760
1868	14,423	3,396	17,820
1869	14,278	3,326	17,603
1870	14,849	3,486	18,335
1871	14,946	3,457	18,403
1872	14,943	3,485	18,429
1873	14,721	3,465	18,187
1874	14,615	3,474	18,089
1875	14,606	3,498	18,104
1876	14,527	3,509	18,036
1877	14,453	3,531	17,984
1878	14,407	3,537	17,943
1879	14,255	3,554	17,809
1880	14,096	3,579	17,675
1881	13,978	3,590	17,568
1882	13,892	3,600	17,492
1883	13,721	3,599	17,320
1884	13,570	3,605	17,175
1885	13,576	3,626	17,202
1886	13,412	3,644	17,056
1887	13,278	3,666	16,944
1888	13,251	3,687	16,938
1889	13,195	3,673	16,867
1890	13,080	3,671	16,751
1891	12,904	3,581	16,485
1892	12,764	3,563	16,327
1893	12,627	3,524	16,151
1894	12,627	3,538	16,165
1895	12,460	3,507	15,967
1896	12,335	3,501	15,836

In the final third of the last century improvements to the practices of cultivation were slowed down or halted by the overall retreat from cereal production. Just how severe this was is illustrated by the table from which it will be seen that in England and Wales the acreage fell from a peak of close on 15 million in 1871 to 12.335 million in 1896. In the face of such a run down of acreage and the concomitant decline in the profitability of the crops that were grown it is hardly a matter for astonishment that steam ploughing and cultivating stagnated for some three decades. Innovators did not disappear but manifested themselves mainly in other branches of farming - particularly the dairy where the avant-garde experimented with improved techniques for handling milk. A milk separator was shown at the Royal at Kilburn in 1879, that disastrous show dogged by rain and ruined by mud. Early separators were turned manually but within a few years were supplied for power working which at that time usually meant a fixed or portable steam engine.

The first milking machine was shown at the International Exhibition of 1862 but neither it nor its successors of the next thirty-three years attained acceptance. Shield's.'Thistle' machine built in Glasgow from about 1895 on had some practical success, being based on the pulsator principle, subsequently much used, but it was very difficult to keep clean, and was further rendered unhygienic by the large amounts of air it used which passed through the same tubes as the milk, causing contamination. The power source of many of these 'Thistle' machines was a steam engine.

Another aspect of farming improvement that had a much earlier foundation than is commonly supposed was crop drying by heated chambers. A two chamber crop drying plant was first patented by W.A.Gibbs of Gilwell Park in 1866 and improved up to about 1880. Gibbs heated air by the smokebox heat of a portable steam engine and also from the exhaust steam, drawing the warmed air through the drying chambers, which were used alternately - one in use whilst the other was being filled or emptied - by means of a fan driven by the same portable as was providing the heat. A series of wet summers in the early eighties gave point to these experiments with, however, limited practical success and a level of expense that placed such plant outside the financial reach of its intended users. Except for specialised applications such as hops, drying crops by artificial means on an extended scale languished until it was revived as an adjunct to the combine harvester in the period after the Second World War.

There were successful innovators. Such a one in quite a different field from those we have been discussing was Harry Evershed (1861-1926), remembered as a member of the firm of Bomford & Evershed of Salford Priors, Worcestershire. Harry was a quiet reflective man, ingenious as an inventor and designer of machines, witty in his observations and good natured in his personal dealings but overshadowed by his more famous brother Sidney, co-founder of the celebrated firm of instrument makers and electrical engineers, Evershed & Vignoles Ltd. of Acton, London. The subject to which Harry contributed most and for which he has received too little acclaim was the dredging of lakes, ponds, and rivers by land based steam engines. This is how Reg Smith, who worked for him as a young man, described the plant which he designed:

"Bomford & Evershed's specialised plant, operated by tried and experienced men, designed and adapted by him, could and did tackle anything that came along. Any and every description of mill pond, lake, river, or reservoir was successfully dredged by this firm all over the country, and I have never heard of a job they were unable to carry out. The variety of conditions they encountered was astonishing; so were the variety and versatility of the equipment that Evershed designed to meet and conquer these conditions."

Harry Evershed was the third son of John Evershed, owner of the tannery at Gomshall, near Guildford, and grandson of John Evershed of nearby Albury, a farmer who lived from 1785 to 1890. Harry spent his early working life with Fowlers, being sent abroad on several occasions to commission sets of Fowler

Fig.26. *A compound Fowler ploughing engine equipped with Harry Evershed's design of winding-back drum. The picture shows clearly the dog clutch drive, the mating pinion of which is displayed by the feet of the two men standing by the winding drum.* [MERL]

Fig.27. *A rather older single cylinder Fowler plougher fitted with an earlier version of Evershed's winding-back drum, shown here dredging a narrow waterway with a scoop of his design.* [MERL]

tackle. Whilst in Asia Minor he contracted malaria, was sent home to recover, and subsequently worked in the Leeds drawing office. He made several trips to Algeria, farmed there for a while on his own account and did steam ploughing by contract but returned again to England in 1890; worked for a time in London with a former colleague, and then went abroad once more, this time to Greece, on a commission from Fowlers. In the spring of 1893 Harry, back in Britain, was sent by Fowlers to Aiton to inspect the work of a Fowler dredging scoop, which he reported to have made a great mess. Despite this adverse report a similar scoop was shown by Fowlers at Warwick Royal later in the same year. In the meantime Benstead, Fowler's leading draughtsman, had been sent to Bomford's works at Pitchill, Warwickshire, to see a scoop they were using which was thought to be an improvement on the Fowler design, and at his suggestion Harry Evershed went there also to pass an opinion on it, staying the night with Raymond Bomford at Bevington Hall. Not only did he approve of the Bomford design of scoop but liking between the two men was so instantaneous that before he left Pitchill Evershed had agreed with Raymond and Benjamin Bomford to join their firm, an association that was to continue until his death. In 1904 the two Bomfords and Harry Evershed took over the assets and factory of Humphries & Co.Ltd. of Atlas Works, Pershore, setting up a new company, Bomford & Evershed Ltd. to carry on the enterprise. It did not prosper at Pershore, and in 1907 took over the R.& B. Bomford contracting plant - ploughing engines and rollers - and moved to Pitchill. Thereafter things improved somewhat financially, though the steam cultivation side of the business lost the money which dredging and road rolling earned it.

Because the returns from ploughing and cultivation were so poor the partners, and particularly Evershed, concentrated on the dredging business with a view to getting better utilisation out of the ploughing engines. Dredging soon became a subject of absorbing interest to Harry Evershed to which he devoted his formidable talent for original design. Probably the most important innovation designed by him was the adaptation of the system for working by a single engine, the return rope of the dredging scoop, which, of course, carried little load, being taken through a pulley held by ground anchors, or trees where conveniently placed, at the far side of the dredging area and back onto a vertical drum on the single engine, powered off the road gearing. Reg Smith described it thus:

> "This was driven off the crankshaft through the existing high gear pinion and the layout can be followed in the photographs in which position and mounting of the drum are so well shown. The stud shaft which can be seen projecting between the crankshaft and the drum carried an idler pinion which could be slid in or out of mesh with the crankshaft pinion and the drum gear, and this was arranged so that when the crankshaft pinion was in the 'out of gear' position as regards the road gear, it was in line with the vertical drum gear so as to permit the idler pinion to be slid into engagement with both drum and crankshaft pinion simultaneously. When it was necessary to move the engine about on the job, the low gear was generally used; if, however, the high gear was needed, the action of moving the high gear pinion into engagement also slid the idler pinion out of gear with the vertical drum. It was all quite simple and, like most simple mechanisms, much easier to use than to describe."

In addition, however, he did a lot for the design of scoops. Those designed by Fowlers had had the operation of the discharging mechanism actuated by hand-wheels, unpleasant to operate and, moreover, very slow. In the Evershed scoops the discharge flap or door operated automatically with the reversal of the rope pull, a great time saver. Besides all this he produced scoops in a great variety of shapes and sizes so that there arose the reputation, noted by Reg Smith, that Bomford & Evershed could dredge any sheet of water no matter how awkwardly situated or hemmed in by restrictions. Reg Smith described in detail one of the scores of dredging contracts undertaken:

> "One of these contracts I remember most vividly was carried out during the memorable summer of 1921; this was the dredging of the mill pond at Broom, near Bidford-on-Avon, for Messrs. Adkins & Thomas Ltd. At that time I was working as a fitter in the repair shop at Salford Priors and, as I was lodging in the village and found time hang rather heavily in the evening, I was glad to gain some experience of dredging (and supplement my wages) by riding over to Broom Mill as soon as I had finished in the shop to put in another two or three hours on the engine or wherever else my services were required.
>
> The job at Broom consisted of removing a large quantity of silt from the mill pond, and also deepening the pond itself over a considerable area. For this reason, the material to be removed varied from very soft mud to hard sand, gravel and pebbles, and stones up to several hundred pounds in weight; a certain amount of blue clay also had to be contended with. It was only possible to approach the pond with an engine on one side of the river, as the gardens of houses in the village came right down to the water's edge on the further side, and it was therefore impossible to even draw the scoop out of the water there. One engine only was in use throughout, this being a Fowler 8NHP. single cylinder ploughing engine fitted with Mr. Evershed's usual type of auxiliary vertical drum. Two scoops were used, both being of the design patented by Mr. Evershed. One scoop had a cutting blade at the mouth for dealing with soft mud, clay, rushes and weeds, but the other was fitted with heavy T-iron teeth or tines for breaking up a hard bottom or uprooting fallen trees which were not visible on the surface. Both these scoops had been thoroughly tried out over a period of years, and carried out the work very well. It was not possible to completely drain the mill pond, because the River Arrow flowed through it; even with the sluices drawn there was a considerable amount of water in the deeper parts of the pond. As some may recall, 1921 was a year of drought; if this had not been so the job might have been much more difficult.

Fig.28. Pulling in the loaded scoop on a lake dredging job, Bomford & Evershed. [MERL]

Fig.29. Wallis & Steevens 3-ton tractor No.2617 of 1902 posed outside the makers' works with a converted horse-drawn trailer of the type with which it was intended to work.

The engine was stationed in a large meadow bordering one side of the pond, and the soft mud and clay had to be deposited in a depression in this meadow at a considerable distance from the pond; the sand, gravel and stones were utilised to raise a farm road across the meadow above the flood level. It was necessary to use the vertical drum, in conjunction with a snatch-block anchor on the further bank of the pond, to return the empty scoop for another 'bite'; there were a few trees which could be used to anchor the snatch-block, but elsewhere a ground-anchor had to be pressed into service. A heavy flat-bottomed boat was a part of the usual equipment on Bomford & Evershed's dredging jobs, and this proved most useful at Broom; in spite of the difficulties I have described, the job went through very well and no serious breakages or accidents occurred. The gang concerned were all seasoned dredging hands; the foreman was old George (Gerry) Aldington, who had many years of experience on dredging jobs all over the country to his credit, and the other members of the gang were Jack Barley, Ernie Morris, Fred Aldington, Walter Sherwood, and 'Jocko' Harris. On the lighter side; we caught a lot of fish (including some very large eels) at Broom and, as the gang were good customers, the landlady of the *Hollybush* was always willing to cook supper for them. We enjoyed some fine meals in the back parlour of the *Hollybush,* and a steaming eel pie washed down with good Warwickshire cider was a feast for tired and hungry men!"

Because the successive mechanisation of farm work during the nineteenth century had reduced the work available to farm labourers and, to a lesser extent, to the skilled men of the farm particularly horsemen, each in its turn had aroused hostility and met with opposition, mostly passive, on the part of the farm workers. By contrast, the opposition which arose in the countryside with the arrival of the new century to the use of mechanised road transport was to a considerable extent classless, and in fact common to all, landowners, farmers, private residents, tradesmen and farm workers. Nevertheless, though this widespread opposition was not divided or fragmented as heretofore into groups, nor was it total, and there were some clearly defined categories of people thoroughly dissatisfied with the status quo in transport and its reliance on the twin agencies of the horse and the railway who believed they would benefit from mechanised road transport. The market gardening and fruit growing trades supplying London have already been mentioned. As London expanded westward the market growers had retreated step by step. At the turn of the century the tide of bricks and mortar that had already in the 1840's and 50's engulfed the areas of Pimlico, Chelsea, Kensington and Paddington, had moved on to absorb Fulham, Shepherds Bush and Chiswick. In consequence the market gardeners had moved out to Brentford, Hounslow, Heston, Ashford, Feltham, Laleham, Staines, Yiewsley and West Drayton in what was then the Middlesex countryside. Similarly to the south of the Thames the once extensively cultivated areas of Wandsworth, Battersea and Mitcham gradually were lost to houses whilst, as building advanced to the east and north-east of the capital, growers once plentiful in Stratford, Hackney, and East and West Ham moved out to Wanstead, Enfield, Barking, and Ilford, and later still as these too began to be lost, yet further out to Hockley, Rainham and the upper Lea Valley.

Each move out lengthened the journey to the inner city markets at Spitalfields, Leadenhall, Covent Garden, and Borough, increasing dependence upon the railways, although because none of the markets was directly rail-served the traffic subsequently had to be transferred to horse drays and vans for the final stages. Since it had already been through a similar transhipment at the country end not only was the expenditure of labour considerable but also the wear and tear on the produce itself. Red and black currants, strawberries, and raspberries, all severely prone to handling damage, suffered most from this system of transport but all fresh produce was the worse for it to some degree. Many of the well-known growers, therefore, avoided the railway altogether, preferring to use their own horses and vans for the whole distance, but the return journey from, for instance, Feltham, Middlesex, to Covent Garden meant an overall daily trip of some 27 miles and a long wait at the market end - a tiring night's work for men and horses. This notwithstanding, nightly processions of horses and vans were to be found on the Oxford, Bath, and Great West Roads. With the easing of restrictions by the 1896 Act three prominent Middlesex growers - W.J.Lobjoit, A.W.Smith, and the partnership of Wild & Robbins - became interested in the use of steam haulage. All of them bought engines by Wallis & Steevens. Lobjoit began with 3-ton tractors Nos.2618 and 2659 of October, 1902, and February, 1903, respectively. Smith had Nos.2662 and 2663 whilst Wild & Robbins had Nos.2617, 2661, and 2664, later followed (in 1905) by 4½ ton tractor No.2826. In June, 1904, A.W.Smith went for something rather bigger, buying 5NHP. compound road locomotive No.2728. Wallis & Steevens were admittedly pioneers in the building of these small tractors, but in the case of the sales to Middlesex growers the possibility cannot be discounted that the example of the Ashby family, owners of Staines Brewery, related by marriage to the Wallises and loyal users of Wallis engines, might have given weight to Wallis & Steevens' canvassing.

A Kentish grower, somewhat further out from London, who found the services provided by the railways unsuitable for hauling his produce was John Wood of Home Farm, Crockenhill, near Swanley. He had

Fig.30. In avoiding wooden wheels the Thornycroft entry in the 1896 Liverpool trials used steel wheels too lightly built for durability. Nevertheless this type launched Chiswick Borough Council into steam wagon ownership. Contrast them with the wheels on their five-tonner in the second trials (below) **Fig. 31.**

Fig.32. Coulthards' entry in the same trials at the same spot in Warrington as the Thorny croft.

Fig.33. The Lancashire (Leyland) entry, again at the same point.

entered farming as a child at a wage of three (old) pence a day and had progressed, by the beginning of this century, to farming about 1000 acres, a good deal of it under fruit, with an appreciable proportion of this fruit land planted with strawberries. Dissatisfied with the condition in which the latter reached market when sent by rail he bought himself a Fowler 6NHP. compound road locomotive (No.11417 of April, 1908) to enable him to send his fruit in season straight from the farm to the market.

Not all areas where steam traction was taken up with enthusiasm as an alternative to the horse were rural. For rather different reasons it was well received in industrial Lancashire. Strictly speaking, this should be considered in two parts, Merseyside and the cotton district, as the reasons for each to take an interest in steam traction were distinct though related. In the case of Liverpool and environs there was a very heavy traffic into the docks, mainly over sett roads and streets, with sharp inclines, making heavy and destructive work for horses and restricting loads that could be hauled. Prompted by the Paris-Bordeaux vehicle trial in December, 1895 the *Liverpool Mercury* wrote:

> "It will be a great day when horses, which are at once expensive to keep and troublesome to look after, can be replaced by a cheap fuel, which requires no oats, does not shy, and is liable to no obscure diseases".

Though the writer lost his way somewhat in the middle of the paragraph one grasps very much what he meant.

Charles E. Duryea, the pioneer American motor manufacturer, wrote at the same time, apropos mechanical traction in general on roads:

> "I regard the automobile vehicle as the next large business, and think that it is only a question of ability to supply the goods by manufacturers. The market is ready and waiting. No article was ever better advertised in advance, and no article has ever proved so good as a self-advertiser. The thing appeals to everybody at sight. It is thoroughly practical, and can be sold at a price well within the reach of all the middle classes. It is faster than the horse, and so will take with the better classes. It is cheaper to maintain than a horse, and so will take with those economically inclined. There is no cruelty to animals in connection with it, and it is correct from a sanitary point of view. It is less noisy on most streets than a horse and waggon."

Doubtless the anonymous author of the comment in the *Liverpool Mercury* would have accorded his words a cordial "Hear, hear"!

Moreover there was antipathy in Liverpool toward the railways which were regarded as having exploited for their own advantage the then vast traffic potential for Liverpool from the hinterland of Manchester and the cotton towns to such an extent that in self-defence the Mancunians had promoted and constructed the Manchester Ship Canal and the dock complexes of Manchester to the detriment of Liverpool. This conjunction of antipathies led to the formation in 1895 of the Liverpool and District branch of the Self-propelled Traffic Association, itself founded by Sir David Salomons in that year. The fathers of the Liverpool branch were a group of prominent Liverpudlians including the ship-owner Alfred Holt; S.B. Cottrell, engineer and manager of the Liverpool Overhead Railway; J.A.Crowther, Borough Engineer of Bootle; J.A. Norris, his counterpart in Liverpool; the Spurriers, father and son, of the Lancashire Steam Motor Co. Ltd; J.H.Toulmin and W.Norris of Coulthards of Preston; A.J.King, a well-known Macclesfield haulage contractor; and Professor Hele Shaw, professor of engineering at Victoria University, Liverpool.

The collective voice of the Association was one of those which lobbied for the reforms that culminated in the 1896 Locomotives on Highways Act, which for the first time gave them the prospect of ridding themselves of their twin dependence on the horse and the railway. Spurred by this victory that they had helped to bring about, the Association organised a succession of trials of heavy vehicles, the first in 1898, the second in 1899, and the third in 1901. The first of these attracted six entries of which only four put in an appearance. All were vertical boilered undertype steam wagons of which two, both by Thornycroft of Chiswick, were coal-fired, and the other two, (by the Liquid Fuel Engineering Co Ltd. of Cowes, Isle of Wight, and by the Lancashire Steam Motor Co. Ltd.) were oil-fired. One of the Thornycrofts was their celebrated articulated vehicle, inspired perhaps by the efforts in France of the Count de Dion and his associates in building *avant-train* steam tractors for use under semi-trailers.

The promoters had had the wisdom to appoint a panel of judges so eminent and so obviously impartial as to place their antecedents above criticism - Professor Hele Shaw, Sir David Salomons, Professor Boverton Redwood, S.B.Cottrell, and Henry W.West, but the activities over which they were required to preside were disappointing. The articulated vehicle, for example, was positively plagued by wheel troubles. In traversing just over 107 miles it had seventeen stoppages for repairs which cost it 6 hours 36 minutes, and of the total distance covered only 71.8 miles were accepted by the judges as admissible under the rules. By contrast the Lifu wagon ran 143.5 miles, all of which were acceptable, and had two stops for repairs consuming only ten minutes. The Lancashire Steam Motor Co's Leyland wagon lost 3 hours 54 minutes in five repair stops. One would have deduced from these results that the Lifu would have captured the market possibly followed by the Leyland, and that the Thornycrofts would have left the field with heads bowed, never to return. History differs. The Lifu achieved no real success at all, the Thornycrofts went on to produce one of the most numerous of the wagons of the first decade (1896-1906) before deserting to motors, whilst Leyland produced commercially acceptable wagons for the succeeding twenty-five years. The troubles of the early Thornycrofts occurred mainly, though not exclusively, in the road wheels. Road wheels built of wood in the traditional manner evolved by wheelwrights over many centuries as the *carrying* wheels of horse-drawn vehicles had reached a state of near perfection. The wheel of a gentleman's carriage built by a London builder was a beautiful thing, redolent of lightness, elegance, and fitness for purpose. In their own way, the rugged wheels of a brewer's dray or of a boiler-maker's trolley were equally adapted for the work they had to do. One can not be surprised, therefore, that early builders of steam wagons, whether in France or England, drew on this bank of experience for their wheels. In doing so, however, they were laying themselves open to problems. The wheels bequeathed by tradition had been evolved to carry only the weight of a vehicle to which the propulsive force was applied via the body or frame. In a steam wagon the propulsive force was applied to the wheels themselves for transmission to the vehicle. This change of postulates imposed live loads upon the mortice and tenon joints of the wheels which they could not sustain, and the wheels simply came apart in service.

This point had been taken by the Thornycrofts and they had, as a result, equipped both of their Liverpool entries with built-up steel wheels. Because of the restrictions on overall weight these proved to be too lightly built to cope with the sett roads encountered on the trial course and produced repeated failures, including one totally collapsed wheel. So, in attempting to avoid the pitfalls of the traditional wooden wheel, the Thornycrofts, perhaps undeservedly, had fallen into another of greater proportions. Lifu and Leyland, with less originality but greater faith in the adaptability of wheelwrights, had stayed with wood wheels. The Lifu in particular was carried on wooden wheels in which the dimensions and concepts of design had been consciously adapted to fit them for mechanical propulsion. Eventually wooden wheels were to be displaced from the steam vehicle field but not for another thirty years. The important change in the wheels of the Lifu which reduced to some extent their shortcomings was the adoption of the cast or malleable iron pressure plate hub (the 'artillery' hub). Subsequent wagon builders used stouter felloes and shorter, heavier spokes. Such heavy duty wooden wheels, in their latter forms, still suffered from shrinkage and consequent loosening in hot, dry weather and also from the occasional fractured spoke, but not on the scale of the troubles of the mid-nineties.

Elsewhere in the design the Lifu suffered from over elaboration, by the standards of its time, particularly in having a complicated boiler, expensive to make and requiring care to manage and maintain. It is a sad but true observation that every attempt, then or subsequently, to introduce sophistication into the design or construction of steam driven commercial vehicles was frustrated by the intended purchasers who simply walked away from them. All the talented and often devoted instigators of automated controls - of whom Serpollet, Sheppee, House (of Lifu), Bentley, Clarkson, Doble, Imfeld, and Roosen are a mere random selection - failed to attract, or, even if they initially attracted, to hold the attention of a sufficient number of people willing to put down cash to purchase the refined vehicles they had designed.

To some extent this phenomenon was reflected in the second Liverpool trial where the gold medals went to Leyland for an oil-fired wagon carrying about 4½ tons, and Thornycroft for a coal-fired 4-tonner. Coulthard of Preston competed with an oil-fired wagon with a triple expansion engine which had to be withdrawn half-way through the trial. In part this failure was the result of lateness in preparing the entry which was finished only hours before the start of the trial, but in part also it must be said that the introduction of too many innovations ahead of thorough testing had a bearing on its problems. At the third trial Coulthards entered a much less adventurous design of compound undertype 4-tonner and took a gold medal. Other golds went to Leyland for a 5-tonner, and to Thornycroft for both their 4 and 5-tonners. In 1901, for the first time, there were two locomotive boilered wagons entered, not by Fodens as might have been expected from their geographical nearness to Liverpool and from their well developed commercial instincts, but by J.H.Mann of Leeds, in the shape of undertype flat wagons with compound engine and a gear drive.

The 1898 trials made a convert to steam traction of the then Mayor of Liverpool (Alderman Houlding) who, to quote John Brodie, his City Engineer:

"publicly stated that he was so impressed with the working of the motor wagons that he would do what he could to see whether the motor car would not be a great improvement to the Corporation service, as compared with horse and cart traction".

In dealing with Brodie, who was a member of the Institution of Mechanical Engineers as well as of the Civil Engineers, he was preaching to the already converted. An order was placed with the Lancashire Steam Motor Co, who had, it will be recalled, won the Gold Medal, for a 4-ton oil-fired wagon with a vertical engine, which was duly delivered in January, 1899, to be followed by a further pair of modified layout early in 1901. Brodie's account of his experiences with these wagons is enlightening as, unlike many men in similar positions of authority, he was already disposed in favour of steam wagons rather than against them. He had, however, all the troubles of a pioneer to overcome. As he remarked ;"At first, owing to the training of drivers and the elimination of unsatisfactory men, the proportion of time lost from actual work was excessive, but this was reduced as the men gained experience".

The first wagon had to be transferred to work involving lighter loads and kinder treatment than was first intended. Brodie recorded; "It has, however, been found a most valuable help in quickly conveying materials from depots to street works in progress and for street gravelling". It was also used in summer to carry a street watering tank and sprays. The oil-fired boiler on this first wagon was soon converted to solid fuel and the vertical engine was found to limit platform space compared with its successors which had horizontal engines. The restrictions on weight imposed by the 1896 Act were the source of most of his problems :

The principal troubles which have been experienced with these motor vehicles have arisen from the fact that they were originally constructed to comply with the then existing law that the tare weight should not exceed 3 tons. It was, however, soon found impracticable to adhere to the tare limit if the vehicles were to carry paying loads, and very considerable alterations have had to be made to them; and the weights of such parts as frames, springs, axles, and wheels have been materially added to, the total weight with steam up and ready for work now amounting to 4 tons 19cwt.3qrs."

This statement is quoted at length as it gives a very clear picture of how the design of early wagons was cramped by the weight restrictions and of what had to happen to them to fit them for daily work. When one considers it in a broader sense, however, the fact that Brodie was the servant of a municipal authority having charge of a police force which doubtless from time to time prosecuted wagon owners for these very weight infringements, the statement must surely stand as a most brazen example of the double standards applied by local government - a kind of municipal *droit de seigneur*.

In the hinterland of Manchester and East Lancashire the initial motives of the cotton firms in taking up road haulage were part of the feeling, long felt but first given relief in the building of the Manchester Ship Canal and docks, that they were being exploited by the railway companies - particularly the Lancashire & Yorkshire Railway Co. - and by the Port of Liverpool. Quite apart from this the steep hills of the cotton area gave the horses a hard time, necessitating lighter loads and reducing their expectations of working life. James Mann had designed his steam version of the Lancashire flat with cotton mill haulage his target. He arranged his vehicle so that one power unit could service a multitude of demountable flats, but it suffered from the defect that a high degree of driving skill was required in order to couple carrying vehicle with flat.

These two innovative forces, centred respectively in Liverpool and East Lancashire, were mutually antagonistic as to motives but complemented each other in the eyes of the manufacturers with the result that a large proportion of the early or pioneer wagon builders were to be found in Lancashire or Cheshire - the most notable being Coulthard, Foden, and Leyland, but the list included also the Bolton Motor Wagon Co; Carters of Oakenrod; Critchley Norris; Entwistle & Gass; Fawcett Fowler; Hay; Hercules; Musker; Robertson; and Simpson & Bibby. Slightly later Beyer Peacock & Co.Ltd, the railway locomotive builders, entered the contest and, later still, Atkinson of Preston, whilst on the Yorkshire side of the county boundary there were the English, and the Verity, and somewhat further to the east the Leeds firms of Mann, and Yorkshire.

Whereas in Liverpool, Manchester, and East Lancashire the emphasis was most heavily on mechanisation of commercial traffic, in London and the Home Counties private or pleasure vehicles had the predominance, and private motoring had gained many influential converts. This is not to say that steam or motor commercial traffic had no place in the scene in these locations - but rather to emphasise that a numerically important element of the motor vehicle interest there was composed of people well

Fig. 34. James Mann's answer to the transport problems of the Lancashire cotton area was his steam version of the Lancashire flat, the engine of which was between the plate frames, driving the rear axle through the gears.

Fig.35. Fifteen Leylands of Chelsea Borough Council on Durham Wharf where refuse was tipped into barges (behind the first three wagons on the right.)

Fig.36. One of the Westminster City Council's Thornycrofts being loaded with market refuse in Covent Garden in 1908.

enough off not to be deterred by the cost if they were attracted to motoring by fashion, by zest for adventure, or by partiality for innovation for its own sake. Every coin has its obverse and it is true also that there were large numbers of the financially independent who loathed motors and worshipped the horse. If seeking examples in each camp one might have categorised the late Lord Montague of Beaulieu in the first group and Sir Walter Gilbey in the second, the latter a connoisseur not only of horses but of every type of horse-drawn carriage and its accoutrements.

The manner in which steam wagon traffic developed after the three Liverpool trials was influenced by many more factors than the trials themselves though the city became and remained a bastion of steam. The Lancashire, or Leyland as it was soon to be renamed, established a clientele there and a Leyland wagon, albeit much rebuilt, was still at work in the 1950's. Coulthard, who also made a serious bid for sales in Lancashire, sold their wagon business to Leyland in 1907. Thereafter the principal competition came from Fodens or Sentinels, though there were few makes that were not seen there at one time or another, but the Thornycroft, one of the most successful and numerous of the pioneer makes, was not much in evidence in either Liverpool or Lancashire generally. In the south, however, they did rather better, with an early sales success on their home ground at Chiswick. Chiswick Urban District Council, following the precedent set by its predecessors, the Chiswick Local Board, had been in the habit of having the domestic refuse of the town collected by a contractor, who tendered for the work on an annual basis. For the year commencing April 1, 1897, they found themselves faced with two tenders of £2000.0.0 and £1900.0.0 respectively, the lower of which represented an increase of £400.0.0 upon the accepted tender of the year before. Certain of the councillors being aware of the vehicles offered by the Thornycrofts, the council's surveyor, Arthur Ramsden, was asked to investigate and report on the savings likely to accrue by using a Thornycroft steam wagon for refuse collection. In due course he reported that the purchase price of such a wagon was £350.0.0 and that, even if it had to be written off over the short period of three years, there would still be a nett saving of £50.0.0 per annum from its use, and that, assuming a life expectancy for the wagon greater than three years, there would thereafter be a saving of £250.0.0 a year. The Council accordingly voted to buy two wagons for delivery on March 31, 1897.

Mr Ramsden in Chiswick found, as Mr.Brodie had in Liverpool, that the cost of repairs or modifications were a critical factor in wagon economics. In canvassing the sales of vehicles to potential purchasers reliability and the cost of repairs became very important matters. The makers' incontrovertible answer to potential customers distrustful of the assurances given on repair costs was to offer to undertake the maintenance of wagons by contract for an annual fixed fee. An early, if not the first, example of this type of contract was that concluded by Leyland with Chelsea Borough Council. Chelsea was one of the Metropolitan Boroughs created by the Act of 1900, and had taken over the responsibilities of the old Chelsea Vestry which in February, 1900, had bought Thornycroft wagon No.8, built in 1898. This wagon continued in use until 1915 when it went for scrap. It was followed by fifteen Lancashires or Leylands, the first two delivered to the old Vestry in August and September, 1900, and the remainder to the new Borough Council. All of them had long lives, mostly in excess of twenty years. The new Council used them to undertake by direct labour the removal of trade and domestic refuse which hitherto had been collected by contractors. The refuse was loaded onto barges at the council-owned Durham Wharf on Chelsea Creek, from where it was taken to disposal points in the Essex marshes or at the Medway or down-river brickworks. An operational advantage of the wagons, compared with horses, was the reduced travelling time between the last collecting point and the tip at Durham Wharf.

Westminster City Council, Chelsea's neighbour to the east, also began its mechanisation with Thornycroft wagons, Nos.11 (1898) and 43 (1900) taken over from the Strand District Board, and No.44 from the Vestry of St.George, Hanover Square. Like Chelsea they went over to Leylands in 1906 with works No.112, eventually having four. Three wagons were withdrawn in 1911, and the last in 1924. The Chelsea wagons were altogether longer lived, six of them lasting until 1930.

In 1906 George Soper made the following comments in respect of the Westminster-owned wagons:
"The four motors are largely used in connection with the removal of household refuse before 10 o'clock in the morning and, when necessary, with an interchange of bodies, to assist in street watering during the night. In this way they work seven days per week with one shift at rest and one shift cleaning. It is expected that the life of the vehicles will be at least ten years. The cost of repairs is estimated at about 10% of the cost of the motor when the motor is used during the day and 20% when used day and night. There is a contract for the repair and keeping in order of one of the motors at $413.10 per annum for five years. The quantity of coal required has been found to be about 36cwt. per week of twenty-four hours per day.

The advantages to be obtained from the use of motors depends upon the need of using them day and night. It is estimated that on this basis one motor will take the place of three sets of horses during the twenty-four hours, and if a motor wagon has the capacity of 6 cubic yards, which is about double the size of the ordinary refuse wagon, with a trailer of a capacity of 6 cubic yards, it appears that with day and night use one motor and trailer would take the place of twelve horses. Under these favourable circumstances, the motor would be cheaper than horse traction, but there are other advantages in employing motors. They are always ready for their work and do not produce dirt in the streets. They can pass in crowded streets with greater freedom and can be guided and turned in a more expeditious manner. The average cost of horse keep for the year ending December, 1906, for the 143 horses, was $2.83 per horse per week."

[The dollar at the time Soper was writing (1909) was at the rate of 4.86 to the pound.]

In practice the three Thornycrofts lasted for 20 years and even then were sold for further use to Edmonton Urban District Council.

Except for Fodens and, to a lesser extent, Manns, the pioneering makers of steam wagons were not traction engine builders. The first wagon builders were either entirely new firms or else firms noted for other types of steam or general engineering. Thornycrofts, for example, were builders of the smaller type of naval vessels and some civilian craft; Robertsons of Fleetwood were, inter alia, builders of ships winches; Lifu had strong connections with the building of both expensive private pleasure craft and with private motor cars; and, perhaps most interestingly of all, Thames Ironworks, controlled by the Hills family in the person of the paralysed but indomitable Arnold Hills, had been noted builders of warships on the lower Thames, a branch of the trade then, in the 1900's, being driven rapidly to extinction by the competition of the North of England builders who had the advantage that they were also the makers of the weapons fitted to the ships, whereas Thames Ironworks and the other Thames builders had had to buy these in from their competitors. The list of wagon builders might be extended considerably. Pratchitt Bros. had been makers of mortar mills; Hindley of ships auxiliaries, small agricultural portables, and fixed engines; Bristol of horse-drawn vehicles; Towards of boilers and tarpots; whilst Jesse Ellis was a threshing, ploughing, and road rolling contractor, and there were many more.

Why the major traction engine firms should have held aloof is an interesting speculation to which a ready answer does not occur. In practical terms the 1896 Act set the threshold of weight restrictions so low (3 tons) that it was extremely difficult to build a satisfactory steam wagon without infringing that weight limit. This was a real problem to all wagon builders, and would have been even more so to the traction engine firms, unaccustomed to economy of weight. Most were also dedicated to the locomotive boiler which was heavy and took up a disproportionately large amount of the overall length. Subsequently when the weight restriction was later eased to 5 tons, the locomotive boilered wagons took a big share of the market, the early fire-tube boilers having earned themselves a reputation of shy steamers. Prejudice may have entered into it also. Pioneering work on steam wagons had gone further in France than in Great Britain, and the French makers favoured vertical boilers, eschewed by British traction engine makers since the days of the Thomson road steamers. Moreover jingoism flourished and the idea of the *entente cordiale* was in its feeble beginnings, awaiting the approval of King Edward VII in order to take hold. There were far more Francophobes than Francophiles which made it distinctly unfashionable to favour French ideas. In particular French engineering was held in great, and undeserved, contempt. The *Commercial Motor*, for instance, once published a picture of a Turgan steam wagon over the caption 'A French engineer's idea of what a steam wagon should look like.'

Thus it fell to non-traction engine firms to essay wagons with vertical or unusual boilers. At the turn of the century Jesse Ellis, who admired French development of cars and lorries (though he never drove a car), adopted the de Dion boiler for his early wagons, a course also followed by the more cosmopolitan Sidney Straker. The de Dion type boiler, though somewhat heavy on tubes, was by no means an ineffective provider of steam. Most of the English makers were less radical and used vertical fire-tube boilers that had served well enough in fixed installations, but were rewarded with only indifferent results because the boiler, satisfactory for a constant demand, was slow to respond to fluctuating requirements. Wagons equipped with it were thus left in a state of chronic unpreparedness for steep inclines or long slow climbs. In town cartage, at which most of the early wagon builders aimed, the runs were relatively short but Liverpool, for instance, included a fair number of steep inclines as well as long, wearing climbs. Traffic stops might give a hard pressed boiler time to recover, provided that the fire did not dull but, on the other hand, the gain might be partly offset by the loss of the steam needed to refill and re-heat the inevitable long pipe from the boiler to the undertype engine.

All the time that the only competition early wagons experienced was the horse their limitations remained not only tolerable but viable. The virtues at which they aimed, and which the best achieved, were greater availability, and the ability, when required, to work round the clock. This was still true ten years later when the author's father-in-law, Douglas Pankhurst, worked at Bligh's Brewery, Sevenoaks, newly acquired by Watney, Combe, Reid & Co.Ltd, the London brewers, at the time when they went over to the use of Standard Sentinels for the delivery of beers from Mortlake to Sevenoaks and Hastings. As first set up the return trip was done by one crew who lodged overnight at Hastings. This was then modified so that the loaded outward bound wagon met at Sevenoaks one from Hastings loaded with empties, the respective crews swapping over. As Hastings to Sevenoaks was a harder run than Mortlake to Sevenoaks this meant a lot of waiting at Sevenoaks for the Mortlake crew, and eventually the changeover was transferred to the Vauxhall Inn at Tonbridge. As he commented "the Standards were very little faster than the horses, but they kept on."

Design rarely stands still though it may mark time now and again. Once initiated, a new product in demand develops as designers find their feet and makers vie with each other to produce improvements that they hope will enhance their share of the market. Quite quickly it was brought home to steam wagon builders that once the initial euphoria of having an alternative to the horse had worn off users wanted, above all else, constant availability and solid uncomplicated reliability without frills in the way of liquid fuels, automatic controls or even compounding unless it could be made as reliable as in traction engines. These virtues were offered by the Standard Sentinel and by the 5-ton Foden.

Competition did not long remain solely with the horse. Within a decade of the 1896 Act competition from heavy internal combustion engined lorries was a reality and wagon performance had to be enhanced to survive. The same conditions did not obtain with the agricultural engine. In Britain, at least, motor tractors made no appreciable numerical impact until the arrival of the Fordson during the 1914-18 war. Hence the agricultural engine enjoyed a relatively undisturbed period from the mid-nineties until the twenties.

Fig.37. A 1901 de Dion wagon loaded with a statue of the French legendary hero Vercingetorix. Note the steel cradle in the rear wheels transmitting the propulsive force directly to the felloes. [N.M.M.]

Fig.38. It was neither raining nor snowing but blowing a brisk breeze when John Russell took this picture of Kingsnorths' Ruston & Proctor No.36848

Fig.39. Beeby Bros'. Fowler (No.2013 of 1873), rejuvenated by an Oxford Steam Plough Co.Ltd. rebuild, taking water at Lowdham, Notts. in 1916.

Chapter 3

As Part of the Scene

"If it wasn't raining or snowing you could thresh" Percy Kingsnorth commented to the writer nearly forty years ago. Work never stopped for frost or wind but only in steady rain because, firstly, it made the belt slip and, secondly, no farmer wanted drenched straw or grain sacked up wet. No importance was attached to the comfort of the threshing crew.

Comfortless though some days were it was far from all bad. In late September, the season of misty mornings, of apples ripening in a mellowing sun, and low golden sunsets, threshing was often a pleasant occupation. It is true that the work was just as hard but the conditions were agreeable. On the whole threshing got under way about then, varying from district to district and from farm to farm. Except during the periods of the two world wars most farmers were reluctant to thresh straight from the harvest field. Most liked to give the grain at least a few weeks in the stack to harden and mature, besides which the other work of the farm could mean that it was not convenient to begin until later. For example, the big mixed farms of the Kentish Weald had fruit and hops, and perhaps potatoes, to get in before it was time to turn to threshing. In a late year hop-picking could extend until October, and the last of the apples might run on rather longer.

In a dry autumn a farmer probably was not in any hurry to get in the threshing engine because of the fire risk. Not only was everything tinder dry but the ponds were probably low as well, leaving nothing to fight a fire had it happened, and also creating a shortage of feed water. The late Alfred Day of Great Tong, Headcorn, used a big old Marshall single cylinder portable to drive the fans of the oasts in which he dried his hops. Cedric Streeten, who was a pupil at Tong in the late twenties, remarked that by the time a dry hopping was over the engine, never an economical example of its genre, had pretty well drained all the ponds within reach, starting with the nearest and working out in an ever increasing spiral as one by one they were lowered. By the time the boiler came to be washed out there was, as a rule, a fair amount of mud to get rid of. Carting the water was not a popular task. It interrupted other work and was a dirty job in itself but it had to be done.

Any engine working on the belt in the days before piped water had to be served by the farm horsemen and an engine that was worn in the bores or rings, or had bad valves or valve faces, soon got the name for being a guzzler of water which endeared it neither to the carters nor to the farmer particularly as the coal burned to evaporate the excess water had all to be bought by him. This applied with as much force whether the engine was his own or a contractor's. Apart from this the relationships of contractors with farmers were always complicated and baffling. Threshing by contractors had scarcely been established when the surplus of capacity created by the agricultural depression of 1879 pushed down hire rates and imposed further financial stringency by stretching the liquid funds of the farmers to near breaking point. As a result they took a long time to pay. After a few years of unfettered competitive price cutting the threshing contractors began to form local trade associations for the purpose of setting a minimum hire rate - which frequently became the maximum as well, as few clients would pay above the minimum.

A typical association, such as that for Kent, would have perhaps a dozen to fifteen members, paying a couple of guineas a year subscription. A member, or possibly a local solicitor, would be the Secretary either in an honorary capacity or for a nominal fee, whilst there would be a few expenses for postage, printing, paper, and the annual general meeting. Such a group might have informal exchanges of view with neighbouring associations and would settle annually a minimum hire rate which it was hoped members would observe. A few did, perhaps, abide by the agreement in both spirit and letter but, as in many such bodies, most regarded the agreement as something to blunt the edge of the competition they faced without its being treated as wholly binding upon themselves. Long credit was sought, and often obtained, by farmers and was supposedly taken into account when fixing the association rate but those fortunate few farmers able to pay prompt cash asked for, and usually got, the concession of a substantial cash discount.

Other topics than prices inevitably came up for discussion at the association meetings. An ever present irritation was the matter of 'prohibited hours', the restriction which Local Authorities were empowered by the Locomotive Act 1865 to place upon the times of day during which a traction engine might move on the road in the area under its jurisdiction. Thus one authority might bar engines from 6 a.m. to 10 p.m., whilst the adjoining authority forbad movement between 10 p.m. and 6 a.m. The potential for delay in such limitations was severe. It was mitigated slightly by the Highways & Locomotives (Amendment) Act of 1878 which limited prohibited hours to eight out of any twenty-four but the scope for official mischief making remained high, assisted by the notorious Section 6 of the earlier Act of 1862 which gave bodies responsible for bridges the power to refuse the right of passage to engines considered too heavy for the structure. This provision, reasonable and logical enough on its face value, remained in force and in practice was administered capriciously, if not with outright malice.

Although local associations provided debating points and gave the chance of moral support and mutual sympathy to members troubled by the operation of these or other restrictions each individual association was too small and too straitened in its funds to do much more. Though it was agreed to be self-evident that more was needed and there was talk for a long while of forming a National Traction Engine Owners' and Users' Association, it was not until 1893 that the Kent County Association took the initiative of hiring Sadler's Wells Theatre for an inaugural meeting, persuading Arthur G.Boscawen, the Member of Parliament for Tonbridge, to take the chair, and issuing invitations to the prominent members of the traction engine building fraternity and to major owners and users to attend the meeting. Kent provided seven out of the seventeen first committee members of the new national association which came into formal existence as from December 6, 1893.

Its choice of a legal adviser was perspicacious. The man selected was William Joynson-Hicks (1865-1932), 'Jix' to his friends and close associates. He was later a Conservative M.P., subsequently a baronet, and in 1929 was ennobled as Viscount Brentford. Joynson-Hicks was later a personal friend of Norman Box, the celebrated heavy haulier, and acted for him in his many tangles with road and bridge authorities. The first major service he performed for the Association, however, was the marshalling of the evidence it submitted to the Select Committee on Traction Engines on Roads, 1896, but his longest-continuing work lay firstly in considering the numerous cases of bridge restriction which came to its notice to see if the restricting authority had exceeded its powers, and secondly in examining cases brought against individual members in respect of 'extraordinary traffic'. In these latter matters he frequently acted with the Association's consulting civil engineer, H.Howard Humphreys, whose ability to confound slipshod decisions by highway engineers became a near legend, a subject to which we will return later.

To revert to the matter of the complications in the relationships between threshing contractors and their customers, these could depend upon much beside price so that even with the county associations fixing or recommending a minimum figure, more or less grudgingly adhered to by members, there were other avenues of competition open to contractors. Doubtless many decisions about which contractor to employ were taken without consideration of competitive elements at all. There might be ties of family or friendship between the farmer and the thresher owner, or the farmer might quite simply prefer the driver employed by one owner to the man who drove his competitor's set. Drivers and customers could both be difficult, and the chances of two cross-grained characters happening to fit in with each other, or disagreeing, was an unknown quantity. Modern plant and a good output was, of course, a prime attraction. Outfits which suffered too much from broken belts, bunged up shakers, or asthmatical engines soon lost their appeal, but though modern plant appealed to customers, ironically, in the depressed conditions of the late eighties and early nineties this was exactly what few contractors could afford.

The pattern of the traction engine had settled down by then into what we now regard as the conventional but there were still some peculiar old relics at work. Few, by present day standards, were of really great antiquity, the oldest being little over thirty years old, but in the period of their lives design had progressed from the tentative to the settled, and the survivors of unconventional layout had begun to stand out as eccentricities. At that time it was not obligatory to insure and few owners did so though it would be beyond your author's ability to advance statistics in support of this statement. Undoubtedly some traction engine owners were prudent and enlightened men able to form a sound opinion of the fitness, or otherwise, of an engine and boiler for work. Others were feckless, believing that trouble would never happen to them; some, again, were callous whilst others were simply incapable of understanding the risks they ran. In such matters, on the whole, like attracts like, and the heedless owner tended to employ men of similar habits and, in turn ,to be employed by farmers of the same mind.

Fig.40. Though double-engine sets dominated the ploughing scene, some roundabout tackle went on for many years, such as this set powered by an unidentified McLaren, photographed in the early years of this century.

Fig.41. Aveling & Porter No.2704 (1890) was an 8NHP convertible, new to George Brotherwood of Tonbridge, but owned for most of the 1920's and 30's by Fred Gillford of Daybrook, Notts. who took the photograph.

Fig.42. Jesse Ellis at the peak of his career in 1900 posed beside his new Aveling & Porter road locomotive No.4555 in the makers' yard. Named Polly (after the nickname of his wife, Mary), it was subsequently driven by him to Maidstone.

Though threshing might begin before the summer had expired into autumn it was relatively rare for all the threshing on an individual farm of any size to be done in one extended visit. There were sound practical reasons for this. Threshing was labour intensive and required the farmer to divert perhaps seven or eight of his regular men to attend upon the threshing or, alternatively, to take on casuals who were generally available but looked at a little askance. For a thresher to have its regular set of casual followers was rather more common in East Anglia and the South Midlands with their large arable farms than in Kent and Sussex with their emphasis on mixed farming. To do much threshing in one stint kept the regular men from their ordinary work for an inconveniently long time and many farmers preferred to break up the threshing into an early, say September, visit, another about December, and possibly even a third in February. This was given further point by the pattern of land tenure in England, the fields of one farm often penetrated by and interspersed with the fields of another, and the main farms frequently having out-yards or secondary groups of buildings. Stackyards were spread around these to lessen fire hazards and each yard might be threshed on a separate occasion, which fitted in with visits a few weeks apart.

Again, even in the days of unlimited competition, there was a limit to what was practicable in the number of threshing sets an area was able to support so that if, however improbably, every farmer had been equally desirous of starting to thresh on a given date and of continuing until all his stacks had been finished it would not have been feasible to do so. There would simply not have been enough sets to go round, so, with no farmer being made to feel he had to take second place to another, somehow a round for the engine and drum was got together. There were always contingencies to be catered for, however. The case of "If you don't get into those four stacks this week you'll not be able to get near 'em for three months", might send a set of tackle off to the other end of its district on a Saturday afternoon or Sunday morning. Then, of course, there was always the threat, "if you can't do my work when I want it done I shall have to give it to X". X's engine might be a beaten-up old 8NHP with worn bores, chattering gears, sloppy bearings, gluttonous with the coal and water, and an engine which no man in his right mind would have on the place, but it was a convenient stick to have to hand with which to beat the regular contractor.

Besides competing on availability and quality of plant owners were forced into competing on the length of credit they were prepared to extend. Three months was quite common, six months far from rare, and twelve months not unknown, with, behind it all, the prospect of a slow payer lapsing into insolvency before he had discharged his debt. The farmers' problems on liquidity were real and were not, or not always, the outcome of personal vagaries. Cash accrued only when something was sold and there were long gaps between the selling times of major crops. Recession made matters worse and the proceeds of selling a year's crops were often already bespoke to clear off the debts remaining from the year before.

If a golden age of the traction engine ever existed it was probably pitched in the twenty years between 1894 and 1914, the period when, on the one hand, the worst of the nineteenth century agricultural depression had lifted and the agricultural interest had adapted itself somewhat to the altered conditions which followed it and, on the other hand, the 1914-18 war and the sorry years that came after it were still in the future. During that period traction engine design reached its peak and traction engine owners found business sufficiently revived to permit them to embark on the purchase or hire-purchase of new engines and drums.

For most of the nineties the arable acreage in England hovered around the 12½ million mark. The underlying trend was still downward but for the brief spell 1893-94 the shrinkage was halted altogether. Much land that went out of cultivation was lost to the growth of towns, rather than to the depression of demand for produce, cheap rail fares and the expansion of tramways having led to vast areas being sucked into urban development. The prospects in the home traction engine market had so much improved, in fact, by the mid-nineties as to attract back into it Richard Garrett & Sons of Leiston who had stopped production ten or twelve years before because of the reduced demand. Some of the new engines built from the nineties onward were bought and run by wealthy men or aristocratic landlords with large estates and some by farmers themselves but the general run of purchasers were contractors, men of humble origin who had, in the phrase the Victorians liked, "got on", progressing from the status of workman to that of owner driver and perhaps then on to wider success. Such a one was Jesse Ellis (1846-1916) who started his working life at the age of nine by driving a portable. At twenty he had his own engine and threshing round, and in 1870 moved this business to Maidstone, the county town. There he attracted the notice of Arthur Fremlin, the Maidstone brewer, who subsequently joined him in a partnership as contractors, Ellis supplying the expertise and Fremlin the money to expand the business. Fremlin died after three months, leaving his share to his widow, but the business continued to grow and at its peak, at the beginning of this century, owned 45 traction engines and rollers, 6 threshing sets, and 3 sets of ploughing engines.

John Shirras was another who began as an engine driver and became a master man at the expense of unremitting toil that made him an old man when, in truth, he was barely middle-aged. With him, as with his wife, traction engines had been the entire backdrop of life. In the late 1880's, as a teenage girl, Mrs. Shirras had gone to keep house for her brothers, George and Robert Scott, at Backhill, Countess Wells, near Aberdeen, when they set up in business on their own account with 6NHP Aveling & Porter single, No.2274, which had been supplied new in 1887 to their uncle by marriage, William Littlejohn, whose farm lay off the Skene Road, close in to the old city of Aberdeen, the bricks and mortar of which were soon to roll out and over it in the tide of urban expansion which has already been remarked on. It was there that she met John as an ambitious young journeyman driver. Soon he was in business for himself using a Clayton & Shuttleworth 6NHP single, (probably No.34001 of 1901). He followed this with a Fowler compound heavy haulage engine (No.11442 of 1908 - an A5 on an R1 boiler), the performance of which he found disappointing. It is necessary to bear in mind that by his standards perfection was only just about acceptable. To achieve this he ordered a new engine to his own specification. This was his three speed compound Fowler road engine No.13138 of 1913 (fortunately still with us) into which he had incorporated a number of modifications required to match his concept of the perfect engine. The engine was indeed a good one, and maintained by its owner in a state as near perfection as it was possible to achieve. Ted, his younger son, related how as a young teenager he had been given one side of the engine to clean whilst his older brother did the other side and his father cleaned the top work. All three worked a long time and eventually father leaned over from the footboard. The two boys straightened up, conscious of the effort they had put into the job and possibly expecting some praise for the result. Their father looked silently at the engine for some time, sighed, and remarked "You lads are easily satisfied, aren't you".

By this time his home village was Drumtochty, in Kincardineshire, noted for its oats and potatoes. Carting potatoes to Aberdeen was a staple of his business, away from Drumtochty in the small hours with two trucks of bagged-up potatoes for a thirty mile journey to the market or merchants in Aberdeen, followed by a trail round the warehouses and mills for the mixed return loads. Then came the thirty mile trip back and the round of the farms, delivering the consignments that made up his loads. Fourteen or sixteen hour days at this work were not uncommon, and no matter how late he finished the engine was cleaned all over before being put away. In an age when we have come to expect much it is hard to imagine ourselves in the place of a man who had begun as an engine driver, had by ruthless thrift and self-discipline accumulated the funds to buy a second-hand engine, had prospered with it to the point where he had ordered a new one, and gone on to yet another, in the design of which he had a say. To appreciate the sense of satisfaction he must have felt from owning and handling this new engine incorporating all the little improvements that he had noted as worthwhile during his working life is almost beyond us.

Steam ploughing offered nothing like such opportunities either in Scotland or even in the heart areas of the trade such as the South Midlands, East Anglia, the Fens, Romney Marsh, Dorset, and Wiltshire, where the engines which had been put to work in the sixties, seventies, and eighties still made up the preponderance of the sets in work. Ploughing engines in the opening years of this century were characteristically thirty or forty year old singles on boilers near or past the end of their economic lives. Most were on Fowlers' double engine system. The last survivors of the Smith roundabout tackles had just about faded away, though one or two sets of other roundabout tackle were to go on for years to come. Of these the most noticed and best remembered was the Romney Marsh set of which McLaren No.112 of 1881, owned by Checksfields of Burmarsh was the power unit. This engine survived into preservation. Though the economics of steam ploughing did not run to new engines, a good many old ones were revitalised by reboilering. To a large extent owners were forced into this step by the fact that the old boilers were worn out to a point beyond hope of useful repair but there was also the consideration that by the use of a modern steel boiler the working pressure could be increased by perhaps 40p.s.i., thereby enhancing the power output and probably the overall efficiency.

Fig.43. John Shirras's Clayton & Shuttleworth 6NHP single of 1901 (probably No.34001).

Fig.44. One of a pair of Fowler singles (2669 + 2670) converted by Edwin Goode to the tandem compound system.

Fig.45. The conversion of a Fowler single (either 1049 or 1050) to compound on the Burrell single crank system. Now known as No.3448 it is seen here in April, 1990.

About the beginning of this century the Oxfordshire Steam Ploughing Co. set about a programme of rebuilding its own fleet of single cylinder Fowlers on entirely new boilers whilst at the same time overhauling the engine parts and the running and ploughing gear. Modern directly loaded safety valves took the place of the old Salter valves and much longer smokeboxes were fitted. The engines so treated were far better performers than they had been when new. News of what they were doing spread fast and in the first twenty years of this century the Oxfordshire Steam Ploughing Co. rebuilt many engines belonging to other owners, and also supplied new boilers for engines undergoing rebuilding elsewhere. This gave them a lead in the rebuilding field but other firms of engineers also took part in it.

Aside from reboilering and higher boiler pressures improvements were sought in the use of steam, i.e. by improving the pressure drop. Though Churchward's work on the Great Western Railway in the use of longer travel valves, shorter ports, and improved valve gear were widely noted and commented upon in steam engine circles, most ploughing engine owners were hardly prepared to go to such lengths. Many, indeed, considered that compounding rather than improved single stage expansion offered the best chance of a useful increase in pressure drop. However, a 12 or 14NHP Fowler plougher that had been both reboilered and subjected to conversion to compound using the conventional double crank system would have been in the 'Irishman's knife' category, not much remaining of the original. Two ingenious conversions were devised which were not so sweeping in the manner of their application. Edwin Goode, who had a contracting business and engineering works at Elmdon, near Royston, overcame the problem by the use of tandem compounding. Beginning about 1904 he converted a number of sets of singles of his own and some belonging to another member of the family. The basis of his system was to reduce the diameter of the existing cylinder by the use of a liner and to fit a redesigned front cover incorporating a gland. Ahead of it was mounted an entirely new low pressure cylinder upon a new and extended smokebox. Other parts renewed were the piston rod, which had necessarily to be much longer, and the pistons. He is also said to have found it necessary to fit a third crankshaft bearing in order to cope with the increase in piston thrust. Goode's conversions were reported to be good workers and very economical, but they were outlived, in the end, by reboilered singles. How many ploughers were converted by Goode is not known with certainty but it is believed to have been not more than six sets.

Another way of achieving the same objective was by substituting a Burrell single crank compound cylinder block for the single cylinder block. In effect the Burrell block was a tandem compound but arranged more compactly. It was, moreover, patented and carried with it the additional cost of a royalty payment. Several single cylinder ploughing engines were converted to compound working in this way. The Cambridgeshire firm of Pamplins had eight engines converted. Thomas Wood of Crockenhill, Kent, had two, one of which survives. There may have been more. To make the conversions effective a higher boiler pressure had to be used. Goode is said to have favoured 200p.s.i. but the Burrell conversions probably worked at 180p.s.i. or less. Compared with a double crank compound they were difficult engines to drive and certainly not machines to be trusted to a novice, though in the hands of those versed in their ways they answered well enough. The solitary survivor, owned by the author, has long been known as Fowler No.3448. Possibly it does contain parts of that engine which was also one of the Thomas Wood stud, but as the original 3448 was a wrought iron engine and the present bearer of that number is a cast iron engine, there must be at least room for the raised eyebrow as to the authenticity of the suggested identity. The engine has been so heavily reconstructed that, in a sense, all things are possible. Besides having a Burrell block it has a boiler built, or extensively rebuilt, by Aveling & Porter, front wheels that are not a pair, rear wheels built by, or for, its erstwhile owners, and a pump that manifestly does not belong to it, though of Fowler's make. However, the original cast iron brackets still carry the crankshaft and the tender has quite a lot of the original wrought iron plate in it. The late Reuel Stebbing suggested that it is a rebuild of one of a pair of 10NHP cast iron engines, Nos.1049 and 1050, delivered to Thomas Wood in 1868, but absolute proof is lacking. In any event, according to the records preserved at Thomas Wood & Son, it has lived with its present identity for nearly seventy years.

The demand for steam ploughing declined in Kent faster than in East Anglia and the Fens, helped into its grave by the way South East London expanded into adjacent parts of the county. Encouraged by the demand that had existed during the first world war Thomas Wood's had had a pair of new Fowler compounds (15422 and 15423) delivered in 1919, but the boom was over in a couple of years and the engines had a very easy life until work picked up for a while in the second war. Their last work for Thomas Wood was on the firm's own farm in 1950 and they were sold in 1953, but, after numerous

Fig. 46. Steam ploughing declined faster in Kent & Sussex than in the Eastern Counties. Fowlers Nos.3027 (left) and 3028, new in 1877, were bought by Baldwin Bros. of Wadhurst, Sussex, in 1922, but did little work, notwithstanding the 'steersman' in John Russell's picture (c.1937). Baldwins' engines were noted for peculiar chimneys as, for example, in this photo.

Fig.47. Burrell single No.1992 (1897) was of 7NHP, and spent its declining years in the hands of Henry Gardner of Milton Regis, Kent, who ran it until 1946. [MERL]

54

changes of owner, survived into preservation. No.3448, already a fifty year old when they were built, worked after them because it had been found a niche steaming the soil in local greenhouses.

If Thomas Wood & Son found scant rewards in ploughing, their work as threshing contractors fared a little better, jogging along through the twenties and thirties but undergoing a very marked revival almost into a year round cycle during the 1939-45 war. The road haulage activities of the firm, formerly in the hands of its fleet of Aveling & Porter engines, passed to Sentinel waggons, first two DG6's Nos.7953 (1929) and 8141 (1930), and then S6 No.8930 of 1934, with help from petrol-engined lorries, including a Hallford made in Dartford, six miles away, by the firm of J.& E.Hall Ltd., in whose works Trevithick had found a welcome nearly a hundred years before. Road rolling continued and oil-engined rollers replaced the steam rollers. The men who had joined the Crockenhill firm as boys at the turn of the century aged with it, watching the influence of the rural steam engine decline until it vanished. The village engineering works itself, badly damaged by bombs in 1940 and 41 and by a V2 rocket in 1945, was rebuilt, the ancient machine tools survived and by a process of adaptation the firm did the same. By the sixties the works co-existed, within a distance of five or six miles, with the sophisticated and automated factories of the Cray valley and, using its old plate furnace and plate rolls, found it could produce rolled steel alternator bodies that its elaborately equipped neighbours could not attempt. Many of London's Routemaster double deckers thus came to contain an integral part made in a works laid out and equipped a hundred years before.

On the very doorstep of South East London engines owned by Thomas Wood, by the Gates of Dartford, by John Gibbs of Farnborough, and by John Young of Chelsfield, carried on threshing until the cultivated land gradually gave place to the urban advance. All carried on until after the second war and the last to yield was John Young who kept going until 1960 but his last years took him further and further from Chelsfield, latterly even into the wind-swept expanses of the Isle of Grain. The estuarine marshes of North Kent, bordering the Thames and Medway, although within a few miles of large towns managed to remain remote and aloof. This remoteness made them attractive as the sites of gunpowder mills or magazines. Curtis & Harvey's Foden wagon (No.1094), based at their powder mills near Tonbridge was driven by George Cheesemore. From time to time he had to take it to another of their gunpowder factories at Cliffe at Hoo, situated on the river bank about a mile and a half from the public highway, at the end of its own private road, traversing one of the flattest and bleakest expanses of marsh on Thames side where a winter wind from the East or North East seemed to carry with it still the bite with which it had left Siberia - the kind of wind that Vic Smith, one of the Leiston boiler-makers, used to describe as "a lazy wind - that don't bother to go round you, it go right through you". When such a wind blew at Cliffe, George used to leave his mate to steer and himself shrink down behind the boiler backplate, coming up at intervals to check where he was heading. John Young's engine *Sandy McNab*, (Foden traction engine No.4752 of 1914) had a roof from which a piece of canvas could be draped down to the tender as a windbreak, provided, of course, that the engine was positioned back to the wind. If it was not then the driver simply had to endure the wind - as the rest of the threshing gang had to, anyway.

But there was threshing in other days and other places - in the peace and beauty of the upper Thames Valley in pre-1914 days for instance, a countryside free of industry, of the dormitory villages, and of the traffic brought to it by the motor vehicle; where, amongst the russet and brown of autumn trees, softened by a low mellow sun and the hint of mist it might have been possible to sight one of Lucas's old Wallis & Steevens tractions, perhaps even *Success*, No.T250, the first made, which he bought new in June, 1877, and which he and his son ran for some fifty years, the exhaust chopped off in a purposeful but unflustered beat, interrupted only if the feeder, in a heedless moment, dropped in a sheaf unstrewed. Then the weights would drop on the governor and the old engine would raise its voice. The clean carbolicy smell of soft coal smoke would be in the air, the drum would hum and rumble and smoke with dust, the passage of the belt fasteners would make snick-snacking noises all at odds with one another, a jumble of rhythms. But, of course, notwithstanding this visual and aural gratification to the bystander, pitching was just as hard a job there as anywhere else; one in which, moreover, you started the day, when you were freshest, with the lightest work, pitching down off the top of the stack onto the boards below you but when you were tired near nightfall you had to pitch up over your head and, besides, take care that the mice did not run up your trouser bottoms. It was just as dusty a job, too, to rake under the cavings sieve there as on the draughty flats of the Isle of Grain.

Fig.48. *Thames Valley tranquillity as the 7NHP Wallis & Steevens single* Endurance *owned by A.J.Ward & Sons of Egham, threshes in the autumn of 1940.* [MERL]

Fig.49. *Foden No.13248 was the companion at Coltman Bros. of No.12684 which was bought by Esmond Kimbell for use with a threshing set.*

Fig.50. *Robey No.28133, (7NHP), new in 1909, photographed by Fred Gillford at Claypole, Kesteven, when it was owned by A.Summerfield.*

Probably the dirtiest crop to thresh was horse beans, particularly if the crop had been pulled up and there were roots with soil clinging to them, but a leafy clover crop was also a pretty dusty job, the mildewy debris of the leaves penetrating the nostrils and seeming to dry up the throat, an experience brought out in vivid language by Esmond Kimbell's account of a job of hulling in the 1930's:

"Clover hulling could be surprisingly hard work and made your engine shout fairish, with a lot more coal-heaving and water-carrying; though here we were able to suck from a nearby trough, which was the only good point. The stack was mouldy and the dust enough to choke even the hardiest threshing man, and it had gone as solid as a board.

Here again, we were very short of farm labour, and for many hours each day my mate and I took turns helping on the stack in our stint below, which was supposed to be a rest from feeding the drum, when one theoretically sat on the engine keeping steam and smoking. The fork had to be inserted only a few inches, and then the clover came up in layers like boarding, needing much muscular effort, particularly as the stack got lower. Feeding meant shaking out each forkful over the drum mouth and letting it dribble through the two-tyne fork, a practice taking some seasons to perfect. We always fed wheat through an ordinary drum by hand, and short barley and oats by fork; clover was almost always fork-fed, especially when it was full of thistles. In this crop there were plenty of thistles, and they floated above the clover dust everywhere, sticking all over the wet and oily places on the engine, which was not pleasant for those who took pride in its appearance.

By the period of which Esmond was writing, manufacture of traction engines for threshing had, for all practical purposes, ceased. What future faced the trade? If one had believed the advertisements the TVO - engined tractor was destined to replace the traction engine as the power source of a threshing set. The practice was different. Internal combustion engined tractors on steel bands were unable to control the weight of a drum well on the road, and could not set it in the stackyard, even with the bands removed, with anything like the ease of a traction engine. Once set it did not govern well. Drum speed would mount far above the optimum before the tractor governor operated and then drop very low before power was cut in again. The drum speed graph would, therefore, have been a series of peaks and troughs, inimical to good work, and trying beyond measure to the feeder. Though the subsequent introduction of rubber tyres improved the control of the drum, governing remained a problem until the arrival of diesel engines. The consequence was that, through the thirties, threshing contractors continued to use the engines they had without daring to think too deeply about their eventual replacements. A development prompted by the tractor advertising of this period was that an appreciable number of arable farmers with substantial acreages bought threshing drums and used them with their own tractors. Subsequently many were to find the economics of this less appealing in practice than in prospect. Moreover many more discovered that setting and managing a threshing drum were not perhaps quite the sinecures that had been imagined.

Lateral thinking by contractors produced one further development in steam threshing, namely running the set with a Foden steam tractor. Esmond Kimbell related events which led to him operating one thus:

"In 1936 we needed a set which could move around quickly in our wide-ranging but not very concentrated threshing area, and we looked at one of Coltman's (of Claybrook, Leics.) Foden three speed tractors, due to be replaced by Foden diesels. Harry Matthews, meanwhile, had been driving Allchin's last steam wagon for a local gravel merchant. Stopping one day to see it breasting Billing Rise, on the road to Northampton, it too stopped and Harry got out. Coming over he said "Are you going in for one of Coltman's Fodens?"

"Might be," I replied, with surprise at how quickly the grapevine travelled.

"Well I wouldn't mind a job with it."

"Alright - if I can get it."

"But what's your figure?" he said, with a startling directness.

"The same as the others have." I said, partly sensing trouble if I offered more and partly because I was rather short of cash.

"Umph," grunted Harry, "That's less than I get now", and stumped back to his wagon.

In the succeeding weeks, however, we came to an arrangement, and he and I went over to Coltman's to bring the Foden, No.12684, home. Then, master-minded by George Wright, we soon had Pickering governors and a larger flywheel off a showman's Foden wagon with dynamo up-front, standing in a Wellingborough scrap yard, and fitted them to ours, cranking the Ackerman steering rod out to miss the threshing belt and making a sliding panel in the nearside motion covering for it to go through.

A Ruston drum and Foley elevator, both fitted with solid rubber tyres - never heard of before - were waiting for it. And it was not long before Harry was making threshing history, often doing a ten mile journey in under the hour. This turned out to be a marvellous set on the road and could thresh for more than a day on a tank of water - when it was sometimes filled by unbelting in a dinner hour and driving at speed to a brook or spring, thus saving water-fetching. But it was not so good in a soft or sloping yard, and getting the rope out from underneath, and replacing it, was a ticklish job; longer than a T.E's but hard to handle as it had almost steam plough life in it. So we had to be choosy where we sent Harry. And after so long at Allchin's he had, perhaps, lost some of his early threshing skills with the eight-horse Burrell, which further inhibited us as to where to send him and mates. Except for the briefest interval down below, they had to feed the drum all day long, because he could trust no one with his engine.

"A little boiler like this one'll soon have too much water in it and be priming if the pump's left on, as there's no half-way with it like a traction's. And if it's off too long, there'll be none in the glass, and the plug'll soon be out." Thus we had periodic mate difficulty, and it came to be regarded as a punishment to be sent with the Foden set.

Nevertheless, Harry Mattews was a wonderful man, who never seemed to sleep and would walk miles to work, as he did not bike and would only drive steam. And the farmers thought the world of him.

"I was brought up, "he would say, "when it was either work or starve. And what's more, I don't hold with swearing. Nor drinking - beer's the showman's disease!"

One or two other owners, including John Young, followed his example and, within the limitations outlined in the foregoing account of working the set, had reasonable success with the idea. The outbreak of war and the revival of arable farming prolonged the life of many conventional steam sets. It made practical and patriotic sense to use a prime mover that ran on home-produced fuel. On the other hand, as the war advanced demands on coal increased and the quality declined. Consumable stores for engines, such as asbestos rings and packings, were hard to get and makers' spares more difficult to obtain. Supplies of the bigger American tractors, of which the Oliver was an example, were offered to threshing contractors through their County Agricultural Committees and were taken up in a good many instances. Owners who had tried the standard Fordson fifteen years before and abandoned the attempt found that the new arrivals governed better on the belt and, with their rubber tyres, handled better on the road than they had expected.

The arrival of the Field-Marshall tractor on the post-war threshing scene was another significant blow to the use of steam. By 1946 steam could be seen to be yielding ground on all fronts, though not yet in a state of rout, but the rapidly increasing use of the combine harvester in the next decade was to displace it utterly, not by other motive power but by destroying the trade itself. By 1956 few but die-hard farmers were cutting, carrying, and threshing their cereal crops, mostly those who required undamaged straw for thatching or for basket or hat makers. In 1960 John Young, the last man known to the author to have made commercial use of steam in a threshing round, was, as noted a little earlier, obliged to give up. Even in these sad declining years of the steam threshing set when few major repairs were carried out to the engines and a serious breakdown was often enough to seal the fate of an engine altogether, there were a few compensations. Of those few perhaps the most welcome was the final withering away of the pursuit of engine owners through the courts by local authorities and the police. After nearly a century of being treated, at best, as a tolerated nuisance to be cuffed and berated for every petty infringement, real or imagined, of the rules, it was at last left alone to pursue its avocation.

The pursuit of this freedom had been undertaken, year after year, by the National Traction Engine Owners' Association and the Steam Cultivation Development Association. One of the matters that probably caused as much annoyance and loss to engine owners as any was the doctrine of 'extraordinary traffic'. In essence this is not difficult to grasp or to find oneself in sympathy with. The road authority is held to have a duty to maintain its roads in such a condition as will sustain the ordinary traffic of the district. But if, say, in a district wholly given over to agriculture it is decided to sink a mine shaft, giving rise in consequence to heavy traffic over roads constructed and maintained only to carry farm traffic so that the roads are damaged then the traffic causing the trouble might be classified as 'extraordinary traffic' and the persons responsible for it called upon to meet the cost of putting right the damge. This is the principle and most people, particularly ratepayers, would not cavil at it. When, however, the doctrine came to be applied in practice great difficulty arose in defining the boundary between ordinary and extraordinary traffic. Those responsible for maintaining roads tended to fall into the habit of contending that any traffic which demonstrably had damaged the roads must, *per se,* have been extraordinary. They also took the view, on the whole, that the development of traffic was to be deplored as, indeed, seeing the way in which road maintenance was financed, they and their ratepayers had some justification in believing. Every increase in traffic increased the burden upon the ratepayers whether or not they had had any part in originating the extra traffic, or whether or not they had benefitted from it. Because it was considered a case to be deplored the growth of traffic was discouraged wherever possible and this attitude of mind bore particularly hardly on the traction engine fraternity already the victims of the irrational prejudices discussed in Chapter 2. Numerous owners gained from the backing of the NTEOUA in resisting suits brought for road damage due to extraordinary traffic in the first quarter of this century with successes that owed a good deal to the legal advice of the Joynson-Hicks firm and much to the factual evidence of their consulting engineer, Howard Humphreys, particularly his joyful knack of turning the tables upon those cross-examining him. The case which crowned their efforts and which had a pronouncedly curbing effect on further similar actions came about as the result of exceptionally hot weather on July 14, 1926.

On that day two ploughing engines belonging the the firm of Alfred Fuller & Sons of Lewes, Sussex, and driven, in fact, by Alfred and one of his sons, were moving along the road from East Dean into Eastbourne. The leading engine was hauling the cultivator and the living wagon, the second the plough and the water cart. Over the years they had traversed the road many times, had seen the development of traffic over it, and had noted the various reconstructions and improvements that had been made to what had originally been a flint road. The County Borough of Eastbourne had made the most dramatic changes in the section of the road which came within the Borough boundaries. In 1923 they widened it from 17 feet to 27 feet, kerbed it and reconstructed the carriageway using a 3 inch thick sub-base of clinker, a road base of 9 inches of ballast, and wearing course of granite grouted with Mexphalte, and finished with a carpet of bitumen and stone chippings. Though of a lesser standard than would be specified today for the roads of a residential estate this was a good specification by the standard of the time. In the words of Mr. Justice McCardie, who tried the case which was to follow, it was intended to be

"a first class main road capable of taking all traffic, whether ponderous charabanc or farmer's gig".

It had, indeed, already taken the Fuller ploughing engines on other occasions. On July 14, 1926, things were different.

As the engines began to traverse the Mexphalte surface it started to pick up on their wheels. Both drivers stopped and got down to examine the road. They found it soft and plastic - in the words of one of them "like a pudding". They were perplexed as to what to do. Their first instinct was to do nothing; i.e. to stay where they were but reflection led them to reject this, principally because they were uncertain as to how far the engines might sink if left in one place. If running light they would undoubtedly have backed off, but with the loads behind, this was impossible so they decided to go on as far as the turning off, to the right, of the road to Beachy Head, a no-nonsense flint road onto which they proposed to turn. The leading engine went about 200 yards lifting the road as it went. Once again they stopped and decided to run forward light to the Beachy Head Road and then draw the cultivator and van forward with the wire rope. This they did without materially lessening the damage to the road. What they must have done to the progress of other traffic is best left to the imagination. The second engine with the lighter load they simply took straight through as quickly as possible, since parting the first train had produced no reduction of the damage, which was very substantial.

As a result of this adventure they were sued by the Eastbourne Borough Council for £255.0.0 being the cost of repairing the road. They were men of no great personal wealth and steam ploughing was in economic decline so that the loss of the case with the costs which might have gone with it could have been the cause of personal disaster for the partners. Nevertheless it was of such importance to owners of heavy plant that it was decided by the trade associations that it had to be fought and the Fullers were backed to the full. Had the case been lost it would have meant that virtually no road in the kingdom could have been traversed by steam engines without their owners being at risk of having the cost of repairs laid at their door as the alleged consequence of extraordinary traffic. It took two years for the case to come to trial. Eventually it was heard in October, 1928, in the High Court in London before Mr. Justice McCardie. The Council alleged (i) that Mr. Alfred Fuller had caused the road to be traversed by extraordinary traffic; (ii) that the engines were a nuisance; and (iii) that he wrongfully abused the road. Counsel for the plaintiffs were Messrs. Montgomery, KC, and Wedderburn, whilst the defendants were represented by Messrs. Croom Johnson, KC, and Moresby. Joynson-Hicks & Co. were responsible for managing the defendants' case and Howard Humphries appeared as an expert witness on their behalf.

The case took two days and to attempt to go through the evidence would be tedious. The way in which the expert evidence for the defence was presented was a credit to the joint genius of Joynson-Hicks and Howard Humphreys. They succeeded in establishing that the specified thickness of 3 inches for the granite and Mexphalte topping had not been adhered to, and also that more Mexphalte had been used than was usual or necessary. In reply the plaintiffs made the point that, notwithstanding these theoretical objections, it was an excellent and first class road which for some three years had carried a heavy traffic without any faults developing. Examination drew out their agreement that all classes of traffic including heavy charabancs and traction engines had used it frequently without damage. The plaintiffs had thus become placed in the situation of the engineer 'hoist with his own petard'. They could not retract from the statement that it was a first class road without laying themselves open to the suggestion that the damage arose from inherent weakness nor could they gainsay what had been said concerning the character of the traffic that had used it up to the date of the damage for they relied on this fact to support their contention that it was of excellent construction. The way was open, therefore, to the main thrust of the case for the

Fig.51. Fowler No.14269, owned by A.H.Tebbutt, Newport, Essex, began life as a BBS with superheater, but before the photo was taken, (mid-thirties) the superheater had been removed. The engine is breaking up stubbles, bathed in the sunshine of high summer.

Fig.52. 6NHP Aveling & Porter No.1611 (1880), seen in the picture leading a life of quiet domesticity in the hands of Clark Bros., Bilsington, Kent, had a more exciting past, evidenced by its high wheels and solid flywheel. It was, in fact, built as War Department Steam Sapper No.21, allowed to cover the miles untramelled by speed restrictions.

Fig.53. By contrast its near contemporary No.1822 (of 1882), owned by E.& G.Nash of Tenterden, Kent, was an agricultural engine all its days.

defence, namely that some other explanation had to be sought for the fact that the Fullers' engines had damaged the road on July 14, 1926, but not on their previous journeys along it. They supplied a theory to account for the fact. It had been the hottest day of the year, the hottest part of the day between 12 noon and 1p.m. and a shadeless length of road. These circumstances in conjunction with the excess of Mexphalte had, exceptionally, caused the road to soften, and the defendants were the victims and not the authors of the state of the road. The judge found that the weights of the engines were not excessive, so that on that score they did not constitute extraordinary traffic within the meaning of Section 23 of the Locomotive Act 1878. Nor, since it was their first visit that year, did they offend by reason of continuous or repeated user of the road. The contention of extraordinary traffic, he said, had therefore failed.

The claim of wrongful abuse depended upon Common Law and not Statute Law. In essence it depended on the defendant being shown to have done something to the road in excess of lawful use. But the Corporation had already had to admit that the road was fit for all classes of traffic, including agricultural traffic and traction engines. They had failed to convince the judge that Fuller's engines presented any departure from this usage. Much was made of the fact that the width of the rear wheels of the engines was 16 inches where Section 28 of the Locomotive Act 1878 would have required 21 inches, but in his judgement Mr. Justice McCardie pointed out that the engines had been built before 1878 and were, therefore, not covered by these requirements. Nor in his view had there been any abuse of the highway. On seeing the damage being caused the defendant and his son had debated what they should do and had decided, correctly in the judge's opinion, to continue but to leave the road at the first available point. He found, therefore, that the damage to the road was the consequence of the temperature and circumstances on July 14, and not to any wrongful action of the defendant. Consequently he dismissed the plaintiffs' claim with costs. The result was a great personal relief to the Fullers, and a cause of congratulation amongst the engine owning fraternity. After this highway authorities became much more circumspect in initiating proceedings against owners of engines.

Sadly, Henry Howard Humpreys lived on for only four years after this victory. He died on July 5, 1930, at the age of 61 after thirty years as Consulting Engineer to the Association. In a tribute to his memory the Committee said "He was utterly fearless under cross-examination..... He was a man of infinite charm, indomitable courage and tact, he had a profound knowledge of his work and his advice was always sound and reliable." He was followed in the office of Consulting Engineer by his son C.L. Howard Humphreys.

Four years later the Association sustained the loss of another stalwart figure that had been involved it its affairs from its foundation. John Allen, of the Oxford Steam Plough Co. Ltd., died on April 30, 1934, aged 78. C.L.Howard Humphreys related how he had heard his father state that "John Allen was the most far-seeing man that I ever knew." There could, indeed, have been few men wiser in the lore of steam ploughing than the craggy old Ulsterman who had seen almost its beginning, had witnessed the grievous setbacks it had sustained in the last quarter of the nineteenth century, its partial recovery, and the near terminal decline at the time of his death. Whilst it would not be true to say that his death presaged the end of steam in British agriculture it did appear to remove, in the case of his own firm, the will to continue with steam. In 1940 the whole of the company's steam threshing business was abandoned and the engines were sold by auction. Had it not been for the outbreak of war it seems probable that its fleet of steam rollers would soon have followed, but as things were they gained another ten years of life.

The use of steam ploughing engines has never become totally extinct though latterly of negligible commercial importance. Post 1939-45 war steam ploughing saw a few false dawns, of which the proposal to use steam plant in the grandiose East African groundnuts scheme was one, but there was also soundly based work, particularly in Germany where ploughing by the use of steam plant remained vigorous throughout the 1940's and 50's or, in the case of the Emsland reclamation project, into the 1970's. This was carried out by the firm of Wilhelm Ottomeyer of Bad Pyrmont. At the outbreak of war Ottomeyer had 24 sets at work; in 1950, 22 sets; and even in 1960, still 16. Ten pairs were reboilered after the war, the last pair to be so treated being a pair of 16NHP Kemnas in 1959. Many others were given general repairs short of complete reboilering.

The area under reclamation in Emsland had a terrain of acid peaty soil overlying beds of marl. By bringing the marl to the surface and burying the peat, tracts of land of hitherto no agricultural value were converted into productive arable land. Begun in the early 1800's the process gained impetus after the unification of Germany c.1870. By the end of the second world war a residue was left of the most difficult areas, including quivering quagmires upon which a pedestrian could easily sink up to his knees. After the war the government invited proposals for the reclamation of these recalcitrant areas and Wilhelm Ottomeyer, already long established as a steam ploughing contractor, was the successful tenderer. The implement which his firm designed and built for the contract was an immense anti-balance plough with single share and plough breast in each direction, designed to be crewed by two men, with hydraulic controls taking power from a centrally mounted diesel engine. This implement could turn a single furrow sufficient to bury the peat and trash under a substantial layer of marl. Because of the yielding nature of the top layer the plough was carried for most of its working life on a 4 metre diameter furrow wheel with the land side on tracks fitted with 1.50m wide swamp shoes.

To haul this enormous implement, dubbed *Mammut*, Ottomeyer commissioned two pairs of 480 h.p. double cylinder ploughing engines. These were built in his own works at Bad Pyrmont on boilers by Gronemeyer & Bauck of Brackwede, and it seems probable, also, that castings may have been done elsewhere. Broadly the design followed the traditions of Fowler and Rheinmetall, but differed a good deal in the engine work. It could be said, perhaps, that had Fowlers ever been called upon to build engines of this character, this is what they might have looked like. As the reclamation advanced the work became progressively harder since, not unnaturally, the most difficult areas had been left until last. In 1936, for instance, on the Königsmoor near Tostedt a ploughing depth of 650mm had been considered noteworthy, whereas after the war a depth of 1000mm was being ploughed. By 1958 it had become necessary to increase it to 2000mm, and by the end of the project a maximum depth of 2450mm was needed to bury the rubbish. In working at this depth the firm were using four engines, two each end, and a team of eleven men. With this set-up they were turning over about two hectares a day (nearly 5 acres). History has a habit of repeating itself, though not word for word, and the Emsland reclamation had about it strange echoes of the Duke of Sutherland's schemes of a century before. The contract ended in 1972 and *Mammut* and two engines now rest in a museum devoted to the enterprise near Meppen. The decision of the provincial Government to cease the work of reclamation meant the end of commercial steam ploughing in Germany as the Bavarian Steam Ploughing Company had ceased to trade in the mid sixties and the firm of Gröger had halted some years even before that.

To return to affairs in Great Britain in the thirties, by the time John Allen died the number of founder members of the National Traction Engine Owners Association was reduced to a handful, and it had lost H. Howard Humphreys and Joynson-Hicks. The need for it was still evident as, though the Fuller case had quietened the urge amongst local authorities to initiate 'extraordinary traffic' cases with their former zeal, the question of restricted bridges remained contentious. Some such bridges were owned by the highway authorities but most were privately owned, variously by railway, canal and dock companies. Many carried weight restriction plates proclaiming they were fit only for "the ordinary traffic of the district". Some carried weight restriction plates in terms of specific loadings and the Association, through its consulting engineers, kept up a minor though incessant warfare to see firstly that owners of bridges did not fail to keep them in a state of repair compatible with the weights they were required to carry, and secondly that the bridge owners were not imposing weight restrictions lower than those allowed by statute. Bridge restrictions were one of the numerous devices used to cramp and hedge in the use of traction engines, and were resorted to by bridge owners of all categories since a forbidden bridge could often increase the length of journey for traction engines by many miles and hamper their extended use. The Road & Rail Traffic Act 1933 Section 30 provided for a revision of the procedure hitherto followed for fixing the weight restrictions on bridges, requiring owners to declare the calculated strengths of their bridges to the Ministry of Transport together with their proposals for the maximum load restrictions which they considered appropriate to impose. Bridge users or highway authorities were given a right of appeal, and once the appeal had been heard it was the duty of the Ministry to confirm, refuse, or modify the restriction to which it applied.

C.L.Howard Humphreys had an analysis prepared of proposed restrictions on all Class I and Class II roads, and all roads carrying double decked buses. He incorporated this into a letter to the Editor of *The Times*, published on October 13, 1934. Out of a total of 701 bridges only 58 were unrestricted and 72 had various restrictions over 12 tons. Nearly half of the restricted bridges, 331 in number, were limited to 5 tons or less. A number of letters were exchanged between the consulting engineers and the Ministry. Broadly the objection to the proposals was that they were based on calculations which piled factor of safety upon factor of safety until at the end a weight carrying capacity was arrived at which had been depressed far below what was sensible or necessary. On December 24, 1934, having tired of the polite parrying of their objections by the reassertion of the theoretical basis of the proposed restrictions, the Association wrote, at the instance of its consulting engineer, to the Minister proposing that the time had arrived to test the respective points of view by the loading of actual bridges to destruction. At first the Ministry demurred that it had no powers to conduct such tests at the expense of the Road Fund, but eventually it was arranged that certain bridges should be tested by the Department of Scientific & Industrial Research. The method used in testing was to provide a steel frame, loaded with pig lead, across the span of the bridge supported on timbers at each abutment. The loading was applied to the bridge from the frame by a pair of hydraulic jacks bearing on timbers, the loading being measured from the pressure in the cylinders of the jacks.

Overcoming the bureaucratic objections and assembling the equipment took a long time and, in consequence, it was not until August 13, 1936, that the first test was conducted on a stone-built canal bridge of 22 feet span, known as Croft Bridge, near Derby. A weight restriction of 5 tons was in contemplation for this bridge. Under test it was loaded to 40 tons before cracks began to appear, but it was not until 80 tons loading was reached that failure actually occurred. The following month the team tested Yardley Wood Road Bridge near Birmingham, a brick arch of the same span, the arch ring of which was 14 inches thick. This bridge was already subject to a restriction prohibiting any axle loading in excess of 3 tons, or the passage of a heavy motor car and trailer of a weight exceeding 8 tons. On test under a central load of 85 tons the deflection was less than ¼ inch. The load needed to produce total failure was no less than 126 tons. C.L. Howard Humphreys related, apropos the Croft Bridge test: "The officials who tested the bridge evidently thought it was going to burst like a bomb for they dressed themselves up in crash helmets and other things." Misadventure attended the test of the Yardley Wood Bridge. The team spent a whole day loading it up and when the load reached 90 tons the jacks slipped so they had to start again. In 1937 testing of two old cast iron bridges, one at Babraham near Cambridge, and the other, Stafford Bridge near Bedford, produced collapse at 52 tons in the former case but in the latter case failed, despite a load of 135 tons, to induce collapse. The testing programme was still going on when war broke out and was terminated in the face of higher priorities.

Underbridges caused trouble too. In 1938 Ross Road railway bridge at Abergavenny was found to have had its original head-room of 15 feet reduced to 14 feet 3 inches by successive resurfacing of the road. This stopped a member from moving a load of 14 feet 11 inches, and the County Council refused to do anything about the matter unless paid for the work they would have had to do. After pressure had been applied via the railway company they grudgingly agreed to lower the road temporarily so that the load could pass but immediately put it back to the 14 feet 3 inch level afterwards.

At the outbreak of the second war C.L.Howard Humphreys, (b.1893) to whom the bridge test programme owed its beginnings, went on active service with the Territorial Army in which he held the rank of Colonel. He had already served in the first war in France, at Salonika, and in Palestine. In 1940 he saw active service in France and Belgium, and was evacuated from Dunkirk, receiving the OBE for his services. At the end of 1940 he was transferred to a senior civilian post at the Ministry of Works & Buildings, but died on July 18, 1941, at only forty-eight, a heavy loss to the Association and to his profession.

Two years later came the end of another remarkable figure who, in a different and humbler plane, had been very important to the life of the Association. For its first ten years (1894-1903) the Secretary had been H.R.Summers, followed by a brief period (1903-04) of Honorary Secretaryship by a Mr. J. MacDonald. This stop gap period was succeeded by two years (1905-06) when, on paper at least, Henry Howard Humphreys was Secretary as well as Consulting Engineer. In practice he soon deputed the work to his Secretary, an Australian lady (Miss M. Ruthven Bell, 1873-1943) who had come to England in 1898 and joined Howard Humphreys' firm in 1904. At first part-time and from about 1919 onwards, full-time, she took over the running of the day to day affairs of the Association which had an office at 15 Victoria Street, London, S.W.1. She never married and the Association and its business were the centre of her life. With middle age she became a very forceful character indeed. Esmond Kimbell remarked of her, "Most members were slightly afraid of her; doubtless, however, she had had some tough characters to deal with during her long career". George Thurlow, the Stowmarket, Suffolk, engine and machine dealer, who had a stand at most of the principal agricultural shows, provided a desk and chair on it for Miss Bell. From this she used to pounce on potential new members. The year 1934, for instance, was a poor one for agriculture, coming at the end of the slump, but nevertheless she recruited, though perhaps not single-handed, seventy-three new members. In 1938, on reaching the age of sixty-five, she retired in favour of her assistant, Miss L.E.Taylor, but after the London office was bombed in 1940 she came out of retirement in 1941 and 1942 and helped to reorganise its affairs. In case anyone should imagine she was bountifully rewarded for her services it should perhaps be mentioned that the whole cost of the London office in the 1930's - rent, rates, heating, lighting etc., and the services of the two ladies - was about £685.0.0. annually.

One of the concessions the Association won for its members was that of being able to insure the boilers of their engines without inspection. This was negotiated by Choisy & Simpson, the Association's insurance brokers, with a consortium of Lloyds underwriters. Inspection was waived in return for a warranty by the insured that the insured boiler was in good repair. Many operators of engines felt themselves to be competent engineers and able to tell whether or not a boiler was in danger of explosion, never having heard, perhaps, of the sound adage that no man can adequately judge his own cause. There was a feeling afoot that inspectors were pedants or, if not that, then cautious to an abnormal degree. There may have been some truth in the latter assertion for, after all, an inspector had little to lose and much to gain by erring on the side of caution. But the coin had an obverse side. There were many sound and sagacious inspectors, some of whom it has been the author's privilege to have known, whilst there were some owners who took advantage of the 'no inspection' concession whom the author would not have asked to pass an opinion on a wheel-barrow, let alone a traction engine. Mr. E.G.Price, a South Wales owner, picked this point up at the Annual General Meeting of the Association in December, 1934, when he said :

"I would like to refer to the matter of traction engines being on the road without boiler insurance. [He meant, I think, inspection. R.A.W.] I have got opposition in my neighbourhood from a man who does not happen to be a member of this Association. He pays scrap-iron price for an engine and turns it out on to the road, and he is working it against us at such a rate that he has forced the price down by about £1 a day. We are making a rod to whip our own back by allowing such things to take place, for we ought to insist that there should be proper boiler inspection, although that is not to say we ought to have the lagging off every year. When men can come on to the roads with engines for which they have paid little or nothing, they can work at prices which are not fair to us. I have had to shut down two sets of tackle for four years because I would not work for nothing, or it amounts to that. I know that if there had to be a boiler inspection this engine I am talking about would have to come off the road. If there is no inspection there is going to be trouble some day, for a farmer cannot tell whether an engine is in good condition or bad when he hires one, for he does not know the front wheel of an engine from the back one in so far as the technical matters are concerned. He has not got to drive it himself, and he does not care who does."

At the 1934 meeting the question was brushed under the carpet notwithstanding Mr. Price having displayed a fair amount of asperity in the exchange that followed his initial comment. But over about four years the Committee came to realise that they had perhaps opened a Pandora's box and that irresponsible owners were taking advantage of the concession to run engines sufficiently unfit to cause anxiety. In the report for 1938 the Committee set out views that not only showed their conversion to the cause of hydraulic testing but also their worry over the condition of some engines then in service:

"It is thought desirable again to make the position quite clear with regard to boiler insurance. The fact that an engine is insured through this Association does not in any way absolve the owner from making certain that the boiler, and in fact all parts of the engine, are in completely safe and road-worthy condition. In the event of a boiler explosion, whether or not it resulted in injury to any person, the Board of Trade would, in all probability, cause an inquiry to be held in the course of which the past history of the boiler and the manner in which it had been maintained would be closely investigated.

Engine owners are warned therefore that the duty of keeping their boilers in a good state of repair rests entirely on themselves. If a Board of Trade inquiry were to show that an owner had failed to do this, he would be liable to very heavy financial penalties.

All engine owners, whether they insure through this Association or not, are urged to satisfy themselves fully that the boilers for which they are responsible are in a safe condition, and, if they are not fully competent to judge this themselves, to call in the services of a person who has adequate qualifications to examine the boiler and issue a certificate. It is highly desirable that boilers should be subjected to a hydraulic test at intervals of not more than three years, as by no other means can some forms of weakness in their structure be discovered.

Although in order to comply with the provisions of the Road Traffic Acts the policy through the Association covers bodily injury to a third party, yet under the conditions of the policy, the Insured is required to keep his vehicles and implements in a good state of repair. If the Insured fails to do this, then, although the Underwriters may have to pay compensation to the third party, they will be entitled to claim repayment from the Insured on the ground that he has failed to observe the conditions of the policy.

It is also desired to remind the Insured that the policy does not cover any property damaged consequent upon boiler explosion."

How much effect these strictures had upon offenders cannot be known. A number of owners continued to operate engines in a very run-down state but to the best of the author's knowledge no serious accidents occurred. Once one has become habituated to a traction engine and used to its foibles it seems such a docile and tractable creature that it is difficult to regard it as capable of devastating mischief and it is easy to sympathise with those unable to perceive that the easy going companion of their waking moments for so many years was capable of one day erupting into explosive destruction. It is not possible, however, to sympathise with those who understood the hazards very well but who, through greed or self-interest, could still disregard them.

True statistical evidence as to what was charged for threshing is hard to come by. The Association was at pains to point out that it did not fix rates but nevertheless published in each annual report a list, county by county, of what, officially at least, were said to be 'average' charges proposed for the current season. These were usually taken by members to be the 'Association rate' but quite a lot of under-cutting went on. Some parts of the country charged piecework, notably Devon and Cornwall, Wiltshire, Essex, Suffolk, and Norfolk, but day-work or hourly work was the general rule. Devon, where the work was scattered over many farms, charged by the bushel plus ten shillings per shift, with one shift charged to each farm. Generally the prices included the driver and feeder only, but in Hampshire and Suffolk the set owner provided four men, and in Wiltshire owners would provide six men and the coal, which elsewhere was usually provided by the farmer.

Prices were low. In Hampshire in 1927 the piecework rate for wheat was 1s.3d. per four bushel sack (with the owner finding four men) but in Wiltshire, where six men and the coal were included in the price, wheat was still threshed for no more than 1s.9d. a sack. Day-work for an engine and two men was at the rate of £2.10s. over much of the country, though in Bedfordshire and the Home Counties it was somewhat higher at £3.5s. Ten years later the Hampshire rate was down to 1s.0d. a sack for any type of grain, but day rates were not much lower. In Leicestershire, however, the rate was only £2.5s. plus 3s.6d. a day for food money for the driver and feeder, a total of £2. 8s.6d. Five per cent discount for cash was frequently offered and generally available, with ten per cent likely to have been given to sizeable customers and, indeed, actually offered in the North and East Ridings of Yorkshire. The war improved earnings from threshing sets to a degree almost beyond the wildest dreams of anyone in the business between the two wars. Threshing went on almost continuously from harvest to harvest. Taking Oxfordshire as an example the daily rate for engine and drum and two men, which had stood at £3.10s. in 1940, had risen to £4.6s. a year later, and by 1946 to five guineas plus 10s.0d. a day each for the men, a total of £6.5s., with possibly double the number of working days per year.

For a while after the war the high prosperity continued, but owners who were perceptive began to edge out of the business or, if not out totally, at least away from steam and into motor tractor sets or combine harvesting. Those who had been brought up to achieve a high standard of work in threshing looked askance or with open contempt upon the samples produced by combine harvesters. The tide, however, was on the turn against steam. The late Jack Rundle of New Bolingbroke, who had a strong predilection for steam tackle, held on to his steam engines as long as was commercially prudent, but moved out in 1947, the equipment being sold by auction on July 24, 1947. Six sets were offered and the prices realised are listed below. Within five years similar engines were going for scrap at £5.0.0 a ton, and threshing drums were being sold for a £5 note, or less, to be burned on the spot for the sake of the metal.

Robey 28172, Foster drum + Rundle elevator	£1,100
Burrell 3704, DCC, Marshall drum + Rundle elevator	£950
Burrell 2256, SCC, Foster drum + Rundle elevator	£800
Robey 42675, Foster drum + Rundle elevator	£825
Ruston Proctor 44835, Foster drum + Rundle elevator	£825
Aveling & Porter 8597, Foster drum + Rundle elevator	£800

Fig.54. *Wallis & Steevens No.7106 - the 2-ton van for carrier J.C.King, of Weston Patrick, Hants, 1910.*

Fig.55. *Kenward & Courts' (of Hadlow) Foden No. 1877 of 1909.*

Fig.56. *A venture that was a few years ahead of its time - the Lifu van and trailer omnibus that worked briefly between Cirencester and Fairford in 1898.*

Fig.57. *Millers and corn merchants took up steam wagons with enthusiasm, even such modest undertakings as Neville Marriage's mill at Warminster with Burrell long chain wagon No.3373 of 1912.*

Chapter 4

Hauliers at Work

One of the cements that held rural society together was the village carrier. The countryside was criss-crossed by the network of carriers' routes, some on each weekday, some twice weekly, others on alternate days, linking village with town or with railway station. In the town the carrier would often use a pub yard and parcels could be left with the publican. The carrier was usually willing to run errands for a copper or two.

Thus he might buy a book for the parson, some writing paper for his housekeeper, a plough coulter for a farmer, or a file for the blacksmith. These little errands continued into the inter-war period and only ceased in the nineteen fifties when such things suddenly seemed to become too much trouble. Many carriers who mechanised their services bought motor buses.Others changed to motor lorries but relatively few turned to steam wagons though some did. J. S. Haynes of Bideford had Burrell 5-tonner No.3290 in 1911 and Jonas Wood, at Ashford, Kent had Foden 5-tonner No.2862 in the same year, whilst Alf Bailey in the same town experimented first with a Wallis & Steevens tractor (No.2899) but went over in 1909 to an Aveling & Porter 5-ton wagon (No.6754) which he called *Progress*. Perhaps the most interesting vehicle sold to a village carrier about that time was the Wallis & Steevens 2-ton steam covered van No.7106 turned out in 1910 for J. C. King, of Weston Patrick, Hants. In this a short barrelled locomotive boiler with high hay-stack firebox was paired with a vertical compound engine, two speed gearing and roller chain drive. Windows were provided in the van sides and a flight of steps up to the door at the back, for use by passengers in true village carrier fashion.

Though such ventures by village carriers into steam traction were relatively uncommon the use of steam vehicles by rural haulage contractors and by the larger country trading concerns began early and showed a steady increase. Brewers were pioneers in making use of steam wagons. Most breweries already employed fixed steam engines and thus found steam a familiar servant. Though brewing was much more a local trade then than it has since become, even in the first decade of this century it had already seen a whittling away of the smallest firms and the almost total disappearance of the publican who brewed his own beer. As breweries grew in scale so the tied house system, which today is in retreat, spread as brewers snapped up each free house that came onto the market to ensure their trade.

In this way they acquired empires with strange configurations, perhaps extended laterally or with detached outposts. Here the steam wagon, though not fast, gained over its horse-drawn predecessor, for it never grew tired. The author's father-in-law, Douglas Pankhurst, already mentioned, began work for Kenward & Court's Close Brewery, Hadlow, near Tonbridge, though he lived at Leigh, seven miles from the brewery. He recalled how the brewery horse team often used to pass through Leigh at 10p.m. with still that seven miles to cover to the stable. Even after that Sands, the horseman, had to unharness his horses, clean them down and bait them up for the night. Notwithstanding this he was expected to be back in the stable at 5 o'clock next morning. The crew of the 5-ton Foden steam wagon (No.1877 of 1909) that the firm owned were expected to put up a performance of the same order. It served a dual purpose. Firstly it was able to deliver to *The Shah*, an outlying house they owned in Hastings, over thirty miles from the brewery, and to return the same day - a task impossible to horses. Secondly it took over the work of fetching in from Tonbridge station (between three and four miles from the brewery) bagged barley, the caramelled sugar for darkening stout, and supplies of coal.

Millers and corn merchants were another class of trader who were early users of steam. The firm of F.Skurray & Son of Swindon bought their original steam wagon, a paraffin fired triple expansion engined Coulthard, in 1900. When they bought their second in 1904 the owners commented that the first was still running regularly and had by then covered some 18,000 miles to their complete satisfaction. Thus it had averaged less than 20 miles per working day, a measure of how circumscribed the operations of such very early wagons were.

The Road Traffic Act 1934, with its categorising of haulage vehicles into A, B, and C licensed groups, and the inclusions and exemptions based upon them in 1948 when road transport was nationalised have made us rather sensitive to the distinction between the owners who hauled their own goods and those

Fig.58. Kent County Council's tractor No.15 (Aveling & Porter No.5961 of 1906) takes up water from the pond at Orpington, unbothered by other traffic.

Fig.59. On a murky winter day in 1923 an unidentified Clayton & Shuttleworth wagon stands on a Thames-side hard to receive bricks being unloaded by hand over the side of Wrinch's Bluebell *from Erwarton (on the Essex Stour). Built in 1888 she was for years a 'stackie' but with the decline in the use of horses went into the brick trade.*

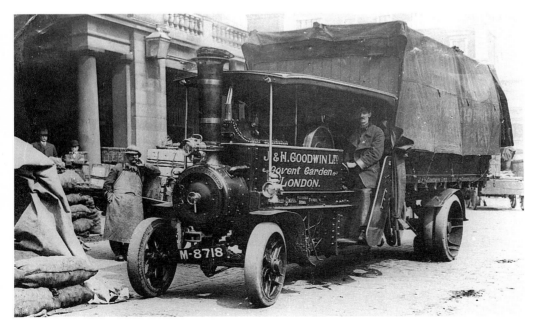

Fig.60. Not far from the spot in Covent Garden where the Westminster City Council Thornycroft was photographed (Fig.36) Foden No.6592 (1916) stands whilst being loaded, her driver still wearing the military great coat given to him on demobilisation.

who were carriers for others. Such a distinction was not so real in the opening years of the century and hardly drawn at all in the last. The Highways and Locomotives (Amendment) Act distinguished only engines used exclusively for agricultural purposes and those not so used. The latter were subject to the vexations of licensing authority by authority, but this had no connection with the ownership of the goods carried. It can be seen by studying surviving county council records of licensing that many of the engines for which licence fees were paid in respect of road haulage were, as to construction, simply general purpose traction engines. Not only was this the case in the 1880's but it went on being so until the 1920's. When Ted Bannister worked for Reeves & Selmes of Peasmarsh, Sussex, about 1920-25, they were using the same engines for roadstone hauling as on their threshing round, though from then on the use of steel shod engines for haulage work declined as Road Fund tax concessions were offered to those on rubber tyres.

Where tractors were used they were the products, in ninety-nine out of every hundred instances, of the old established traction engine firms. Many of the tractors sold prior to 1914 were taken for roadstone cartage either by councils setting up direct labour departments or by firms engaged on hauling stone by contract. On the whole the arrival of these tractors diverted work away from traction engines which, prior to the arrival of the steam tractors in county council roads departments, had done a substantial proportion of the contract work although some had been carried out by horse-drawn carts. Road authorities, indeed, often gave preference to the tenders of hauliers who undertook to use horses, rather than engines, on the ground that they did less damage to the roads over which the loads were led. Not all county councils went wholeheartedly for direct labour and the ownership of their own engines, and some declined to own either tractors or rollers. Dorset County Council, for instance, adhered firmly to the policy of hiring rollers and having stone supply and cartage undertaken by contract whilst Wiltshire also put out much of its work to contract. County Councils were responsible, however, only for main roads, which, loosely, are those roads now classified. All others were maintained by the boroughs or the urban or rural district councils in whose areas they were situated. Though some of these owned plant most of them continued to use hired equipment. The situation changed somewhat after the 1914-18 war which had not only provided a vast stimulus to mechanically propelled traffic but had also given new point to the use of tar bound macadam or to tarspraying and gritting of road surfaces. Ready access to the numbers of secondhand steam wagons and tractors surplus from military requirements, of which local authorities were allowed first pick, and the availability of Government loans to finance such purchases led to a great many authorities becoming owners to the detriment of their erstwhile contractors.

These fluctuations in the demands of local authorities for the services of hirers and contractors were very much against the interests of those engaged in the trade and sent a number into insolvency, but fortunately roadwork was not the sole provider of work to the haulage trade, important though it was to some individual firms. A further source of income arose as towns and cities expanded. The growth of the west and north-west suburbs of London encouraged up-river barge traffic on the Thames taking cement, lime, and bricks from the cement works on the Medway and the brickfields of North Kent and East Anglia to be transhipped at wharves in Fulham or Hammersmith to road transport. Dick Bateman wrote of his experiences as the driver of an Aveling & Porter road locomotive on this type of work in the second decade of this century:

"The firm I worked for was X.Y.Z. Transport of Carnwath Road, Fulham, near Wandsworth bridge. They had two seven horse three-speed Avelings, two Aveling wagons, and one Foden wagon, as well as some petrol lorries. This firm was formed by one of the directors of the old Pedrail Haulage when that concern closed down; their premises were in Wyfold Road, Fulham, Their Aveling locos weighed 12tons 15cwt. empty, and this was to be within the 14-ton limit when working, but they would have been better for being a couple of tons heavier. They were very powerful, being the slide valve compounds.

The foreman at the X.Y.Z. was a boilermaker by trade (his father was boilermaker to Jesse Ellis of Maidstone) and he was also a top-notch driver. When he was a driver short and was taking one of the engines out himself, we used to say that the old engine stood and trembled when he got up on it; as a driver he was in a class of his own.

I got caught at Acton going eight miles and a fraction per hour and was fined £1.10s.0d.; a traction engine in a town was limited to 2m.p.h. I was running on one job from Fulham to Golders Green with ballast, cement, kerbing etc. for road making; and often on the same job would be an eight-horse Burrell belonging to Clements, Knowling & Co., Goat Wharf, Brentford. We used to go up Notting Hill on the first journey in the morning, and if the wood paving was dry it was all well and good; but if it was greasy it was sand all the way up. One memorable morning the old Burrell reached the hill with 40 tons of cement, and the driver just opened her out wide in the third speed. Usually we put any road engine in middle wheel with a load here, and as the driver said "Old Charlie Burrell shouted, but he kept gnawing until he reached the top; he was then well warmed up, and kept going."

Of mishaps he wrote: "As the Golders Green job lasted, I suppose, about two years, we had an incident or two in that time. We used to go through Kilburn on to the Finchley Road, which had a switchback or two in it, and one day the

Fig.61. Horace Viney was a fierce local patriot and a staunch supporter of the Leyland marque, particularly steam. When Leyland failed to make an entry to the Commercial Motor steam run in 1926 he put in, at his own expense, one of his own veterans.

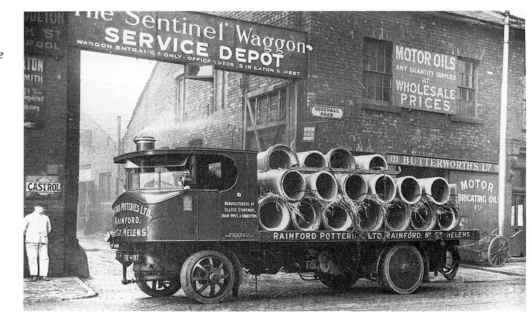

Fig.62. The entrance of Stott's Sentinel service depot in Vauxhall Road, Liverpool. The D.G.Sentinel in the foreground in No.7666 (delivered new in January, 1929) to Rainford Pottery Ltd.

Fig.63. Foden No.385 of Warners Brick & Tile Co.,Knowl Hill, Maidenhead, driven by Teddy Mead.

steersman looked back as we got to the bottom of one of these dips and he said something about a truck. Looking back, I saw the rear truck alongside and passing the front truck. Luckily the road was rising, but the near front corner of the truck hit the engine offside hind wheel hard enough to slew the engine front wheels bang into the kerb, but, however, no damage was done. The cause was that the short coupling pin which belonged in the engine front coupling had got put in the back truck's coupling and the pushing it got on the descent of these inclines worked it up and out, letting the truck free. In another incident on this job, the sister engine was loaded when the axle broke inside the pin boss and she settled down like a tired horse, but her rest didn't last long for a new axle was put in next day, and then it was business as usual. A typical day's work was to go to Hammersmith to load 25 tons of cement for Gerrards Cross. You got loaded, and stopped for breakfast along Acton Vale, and then the next stop would be to shift wheel at the hill up on to Ealing Common (and you hoped it would be dry). One morning there had been a white frost, so the old Aveling slipped, and we had to uncouple to take the trucks up one at a time, putting a block behind the hind wheel of the truck to be left. Of course, while we were easing back to get the coupling pin out, the block slipped from behind the wheel and away went 10 tons of cement down Acton Hill. The truck had nearly run out of momentum when it locked round and would have gone over had not a tram standard kept it upright. So finely balanced was it that three of us pushing on the side were able to return it to its other two wheels. Of course, by then a tram had been kept waiting, but the driver was a good sport, and said that if we hooked a sling chain on the back of the tram he would take the truck up for us. He did so easily - shows the strength of the trams.

Some time later an incident occurred which was caused by the constant chatter set up by running iron tyres on stone setts. This used to wear away the linch pins in the truck axles, and going down Hillingdon Hill one morning off came a truck hind wheel. If you were obstructing the trams their breakdown gang would come along and pick you up, but on this occasion the tram just had an inch or two clearance, so this meant work for us. The mate on the back truck let fly at the steersman, saying that if he had kept the wheel out a bit on those setts the trams couldn't have passed. They then used a lot of bad language and we got to work.

The next stop was the *Dog and Duck* at Denham, kept in those days by Jack Woodley, who always came out with a jug of tea, and here the fire was cleaned and the tank filled with water. Then on to the foot of Redhill, where you shifted wheel.These engines would take 25 tons up here in middle wheel, which I thought was pretty good, seeing they weren't big eight horse engines. After that you put her in big wheel for the rest of the journey,although there was one dip where the road rose up to the Common where a change should have been made. If the road was dry and clear, I let the old engine down here at a risky speed and then before she lost speed starting to climb the facing incline, I very carefully opened the regulator and then as she picked up revs I gave her the lot and she was over the top in long leg. I wouldn't advise this lark because one day if you pushed your luck too far up would come the water and out would go one cylinder cover. The return journey was usually in the dark, and a fill up of water would see you home to Fulham. On the way crossing Ealing Common you had tramlines both sides and a row of lamp standards up the middle. The space between the kerb and lines was too small to allow a tram to pass, so we had to cross to the middle between the lamp standards to get the tram by. This was the chance the old bitch had been waiting for and bang would go a gauge glass and often the other one would bust too. After she had had her fun she would go home like an angel."

Whilst working for X.Y.Z. he encountered most of the road engines working into West London and got to know many of the drivers. With steam rolling and steam haulage rapidly on the increase promising young men had little bother in securing promotion to the status of driver. So far as his own employers were concerned their engines were well looked after and drivers who did not take care of them soon found their talents directed elsewhere, but no one minded their high spirited young men having a laugh and a little fun. With regard to the other drivers and engines he met he remarked :

"The firm of Lalonde Brothers & Parham of Weston-super-Mare had Fowlers for furniture removing, and these were always to be seen. Then a firm called the London Traction Haulage Co. had a ten-horse Fowler; I saw it the last time in Hammersmith with a big load of girders.

A bit out in the country a firm of brickmakers, Warners of Knowl Hill, near Maidenhead, had two Foden road locos named *Morning Star* and *North Star* and a Fowler *Evening Star*; and I believe they also had a single cylinder Aveling. Near them was Cooper's brickyard, who had a Burrell two-speed eight-horse, and later on the well-known Burrell *Endurance*.

Coming a bit nearer to London, a brick firm (Reids of Iver) had a Tasker eight-horse. She used to roar like a whirlwind as if she had holes all over her firegrate, and the driver used to say: "I put a three-quarter Penberthy injector on when I leave the brickfield and I don't turn it off till I get back". He never said how much coal he used!

Pilgrims of Reading had the first Foden wagon running on the Bath Road. Another brickworks at Stockley, West Drayton (the old name being Starval), owned by Broad Harris & Co., had two or three Fowlers on hire delivering bricks. The lessee of the brickworks was J.Goodman, who. I believe, hired the engines from Gravens of Ely, as at least one travelled about with Graven's nameplate on as owners. [I think he has misunderstood the situation. Engines on hire purchase usually carried a plate bearing the name of the firm from which they were being purchased in association with the description 'Owners and Lessors' or something similar. R.A.W.]. This engine was called *Tertius*; who Tertius was I never found out, but if he was an old Greek god he certainly wasn't the God of Silence, for the old engine could be heard miles away! I think she was a ten-horse; anyway she could handle three trucks of bricks. This engine was driven by a pal of mine. A typical day's work was three trucks of bricks to Acton in the morning, then back to the yard where three more stood loaded for Beaconsfield in the afternoon. You had to get a move on, and finally my pal got summoned for speeding; and as he hadn't got the money to pay the fine he had to do seven days. As he said afterwards, "No more brick cart for me!"

Another brickworks had a Wallis eight-horse expansion engine. The driver said he liked this engine, but the trucks shed their wheels too often. A firm at Acton had several tractors, chiefly Fosters; they also had an eight-horse Burrell and the saying was that old Joe the driver had got her in such good nick that if you didn't see the flywheel turning you wouldn't know she was running. This was out of gear, of course. A firm in London had a seven-horse three-speed Aveling, chiefly on ash haulage."

The perennial problem of all of them was where to find water in essentially built-up areas.

Fig.64. S.& J.Trounson's Foden *(No.1166)* Pride of the West *posed with driver Art Pethick and mate Ben Phillips(left) in a placid Cornish village scene pre-1914. The wagon delivered wholesale groceries to village shops from its owners' warehouse in Redruth.*   [John Trounson]

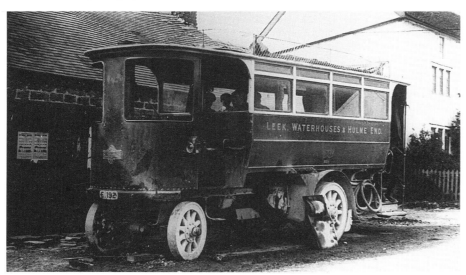

Fig.65. One of the pair of Straker buses used by the North Staffordshire Railway between Leek Station and Waterhouses.

Fig.66. A Sheppee works wagon on hire to Foster, Coverdale & Co.Ltd, the York mineral water makers, in the 1914-18 war.

"We used to fill up before leaving the yard, and this would take us outside London or to some place or some firm where we could get more water. The places were usually a pub horse trough (charge 6d.); one noted pub was *The George* at Chiswick, or the pub at Hounslow. If going on the Uxbridge Road we ran to the pond near the *Adam and Eve* or the *Dog and Duck* at Denham; if going Finchley Road way we made a detour round to Hoop Lane, where there was a stream, or called at *The Welsh Harp* at Hendon.

The driver of Clements, Knowling's Burrell loco had a permit to take water from the canal, but usually there was water on the road on jobs we ran to; but on the run from Hammersmith to Golders Green we had a two-wheel water cart with about 300 gallons. This was necessary when going out loaded, as there was a bit of climbing to go. There was no official scheme by the Metropolitan Water Board for taking water from hydrants, but there was a fine of £25 if you got caught! I have a faint idea of an arrangement whereby if the firm owning engines paid £10 or £12 the water company fitted you up with a meter standpipe, but I never saw one or knew anyone that had one. We all had a key, and the great thing was, don't get caught!!"

Wagons presented a more diverse picture though it is true that, despite the extraordinary number of early wagon builders, few of their designs earned sufficient orders to justify quantity production. Many indeed never progressed beyond a prototype. Yet after discounting these there still remained a considerable number of makers. Jesse Ellis of Maidstone, for instance, built an estimated forty-five wagons from 1896 to the cessation of production in 1907. By contrast, Sheppee of York, in a period of ten years ending with the outbreak of war in 1914, built no more than about fourteen wagons, making use of his almost continuously evolving flash steam generator, yet his lorries were probably the most advanced technically until the arrival of Doble on the commercial vehicle scene. Though vehicle production by Sheppee stopped in 1914 the firm itself has continued until the present day, now making machines for annealing glass bottles during manufacture. About twenty-five years ago Tom Notley, who had worked on the building of these wagons, discussed with the author their shortcomings. Almost none of their failures occurred in the engine and gearing, he recalled, but most frequently in the liquid fuel burners or in the tubes of the flash generator. The formation of scale and the blocking of jets in the burners, either from this scale or from carbonising, formed a high percentage of the faults closely followed by burning out of the generator tubes or failure of their joints. Many of these temporary breakdowns could be overcome by a determined driver provided he was also a competent mechanic but such drivers were never common. As Tom remarked "Every time you made a wagon you had to make a driver to go with it".

Most operators of traction engines and rollers knew, or believed they did, the greater part of what there was to know about operating overtype engines on locomotive boilers, and to such individuals or firms the early Foden overtype wagon had immediate appeal as also, albeit in a more restricted field, did Mann's steam carts. The features peculiar to the Foden design, mostly their system of attaching the frame to the boiler at the front end, were protected by their Patent 20137 of 1901. They clearly considered this to be a key patent, and when Nayler of Hereford began the building of overtype wagons, and of tractors based on the same design, Fodens protested to them in terms so forcible as to cause Naylers to discontinue the building of overtype wagons altogether. Fodens erred, however, in attempting to apply the same treatment to Wallis & Steevens in 1907. The Wallis family resisted the suggestion that their wagons were an infringement of the Foden patent and, since the Foden camp would not back off, the matter was decided in the courts. The decision, upheld on appeal, went against Foden. Broadly speaking, it held that while the Fodens' patent was valid for the specific details it covered it did not constitute a master patent nor confer on them the sole rights in respect of overtype wagons as a class.

A direct consequence of this verdict was the launching of overtype wagon designs by Garretts, Aveling & Porter, Taskers, and a little later, Straker. The first three were established traction engine firms and fellow members of the Agricultural Engineers Association. Sidney Straker was neither. He had devoted some ten years to a design of undertype often labelled mediocre but some examples of which confounded their critics and had long lives. Two new boilers for Straker 7-ton undertypes were supplied by Abbotts, the boilermakers, of Newark, to the United Alkali Co.Ltd. in Bristol as late as 1930. Sidney Straker was a shrewd engineer, perhaps marred a little by opportunism, but not a charlatan. His reputation was clouded for some years by his earlier association, as consulting engineer, with the London Steam Bus Syndicate, launched by the celebrated or notorious Harry J.Lawson, an example of guilt by association.

Though Straker undertypes were not the abysmal failure which some undertypes were, they had some tiresome features. The most directly documented were the two steam buses bought by the North Staffordshire Railway Company to provide a service between Leek Station and the Waterhouses terminal of the 2 foot 6 inch gauge Leek & Manifold Light Railway pending the opening of the standard gauge line between these two points. They entered service on the opening day of the light railway (Monday,

June 27,1904) and ran until the link was completed on July 1, 1905. The two buses, registered E192 and E223 (the latter bearing the works no.114), were smartly turned out, in madder lake, lined in yellow, below the waist, and cream above, which must have looked quite handsome. One of them distinguished itself by breaking down on the opening day, and they jointly earned the reputation of being unreliable, but the thing held most against them was the discomfort of their riding and the vibration which they set up in properties alongside their route. It is said that window displays in Leek shops had been known to collapse from this cause as the bus went by. For a time after they became redundant at Leek they were tried at Hanley for pleasure trips but, these having failed to attract sufficient patrons, the buses were sold to Arthur Wedgwood of Burslem who converted them into vans.

According to his son they were quite fast. His father reckoned he had covered a mile in 3 minutes in one of them, and Arthur (Junior) himself recalled instances of 16 or 17 miles having been covered in an hour, but the wear and tear on the road gear and the other mechanical parts was excessive. Aside from this, however, there were unnecessary shortcomings in the layout of the boilers and pipework. In 1904 when the buses were built steam wagon design was, admittedly, in an experimental and evolutionary phase, but the general principles of steam management were well understood, yet the Straker vans had defects in their steam supply layout which would not have been found had adequate thought been given to it. For instance, the regulator valve was placed between the boiler and superheater. It was, perhaps, fortunate that the latter was not a very effective device or the consequences of this arrangement might have been worse than they actually were. It created enough difficulty as it was, as the volume of steam in the system made the wagons very slow to respond to the closing of the regulator. Correspondingly, when the throttle was opened the amount of steam required to fill the steam pipes produced a perceptible interval before anything happened at the engine. The consequences of priming at a time when the superheater was thoroughly hot can be imagined and were described by Arthur (Junior) as "progress by leaps and bounds". Again, when the regulator was opened after the wagon had been standing with a bright fire, any condensate in the valve and pipe was flashed into steam, resulting in a kangaroo take-off and a sprint of about 100 feet unless the driver was quick with the reversing lever. Aside from all these undesired effects the superheater burned out more rapidly than it need have done because of the time it spent with no steam in it when the wagon was not in motion. All of these self-inflicted wounds could have been avoided had the Straker drawing office placed the throttle valve on the outlet end of the superheater.

Such displays of temperament tended to give undertype steam wagons, as a class, a very dubious reputation for dependability compared with the Foden overtype. This excellence, however, depended on the design of the engine as a whole, rather than solely upon the use of the overtype layout. The Wallis & Steevens overtype, for instance, was a disappointingly sluggish performer because of its makers' predilection for, if not outright obsession with, low working pressures. Surprise at its poor performance was made greater by the good repute of Wallis & Steevens general purpose engines, by the high esteem in which the firm's integrity was held by its customers, and by the admiration widely felt for the spirited stand it had put up to Fodens in the legal battle over the overtype patent. Somewhat later the Clayton & Shuttleworth overtype was another wagon that failed to live up to its users' expectations. The late Harold Darby, who had plenty of experience of the Clayton owned by his father characterised it as "All right for councils and such but no use for anyone with work to do." Neither the Wallis nor the Clayton was useless, but both fell short of the standard set by Fodens.

So far as the better examples of early makes of undertypes such as Leyland, Coulthard, St.Pancras, Thornycroft, and Londonderry were concerned, the modest degree of success they had achieved by 1904/05 through patient development was overshadowed in the eyes of potential purchasers by the spate of very hastily conceived, indifferent or downright useless undertypes then launched on to the market, and it was not until the arrival on the scene of the Sentinel in 1906 that the fortunes of the undertype began to be redeemed. As for the exponents of flash steam, Serpollet; SM; Sheppee; Critchley-Norris; Bellis & Morcom; and Clarkson, only the latter succeeded in selling a worthwhile number of vehicles (about 350 between 1899 and 1920), and that only by owning and operating the substantial *National* fleet of steam buses. For a short time the idea of the captive operating company was also used by Serpollet's successors who operated buses in both Paris and London, the latter under the fleet name *Metropolitan,* but the hills of the Northern suburbs found the *Metropolitan's* steamers unable to keep up with the opposition's motor buses. Serpollet's flash steam generators had done very well in private and racing cars, and performed quite effectively in the self-contained steam tramcars which he supplied for use in Paris, though these were later reboilered by Purrey using his dry-back water-tube boilers. Because of the long-standing resistance of the municipal authorities of Paris to the use of electric trams, self-contained steam cars, plus a few driven by compressed air, had a long reign in that city that did not end finally until 1919. Serpollet and his successors also built a number of lorries with flash boilers but despite Serpollet's work and personal prestige, French steam wagon makers generally did not use flash steam generators. Serpollet type generators, however, had been used in early Le Blant vehicles, relatively light vans probably of no more than 20 to 30cwt. carrying capacity. The main interest of Le Blant, who was an engineer with Societé Franco-Belge, the builders of railway and tramway locomotives, was in developing enclosed steam tractors to haul road trains for passengers and goods that would fulfil the functions of a roadside tramway, of the type widespread in France, in areas where it was anticipated that the available traffic would not be able to sustain the cost of permanent way. For these tractors he turned to double drum water-tube boilers built by Niclausse, the suppliers of boilers to French warships.

The French builders had a start over their British counterparts. Most began with steam cars or steam carriages and went on later to goods vehicles. For example, the firm founded by Count de Dion, after beginning in cycles and tri-cars, went on to *avant-train* tractors, designed to take the place of the front wheels and front lock of a barouche or other private carriage so as to convert it to a steam-propelled articulated conveyance. From these they went on to offer a purpose built articulated goods vehicle but, meeting unlooked for snags, as did Thornycroft in exploring the same ground, soon turned to the rigid steam lorry and steam buses. For their time their success was quite phenomenal, 300 lorries and buses being sold by 1900, but de Dion and Bouton, though not Trepardoux, the third partner in the firm, had by that time transferred their attention to the internal combustion engine, and first steam cars, and then steam commercials, were dropped from production. The last steam commercial probably appeared about 1905, just as the trickle of British designs of steam wagons became a torrent.

This early success of the de Dion wagons owed much to the design of the boiler, a series of concentric cylinders arranged to form an inner and outer water vessel joined by short radial water-tubes crossing the path of the flue gases. The top tubes, containing steam only, did not have a long life but the boilers were able to produce steam effectively and were used, as we have seen, by Sidney Straker and some others of the early British builders. Jesse Ellis used a de Dion boiler in his chain drive wagon and a modified version of the boiler was fitted by Robertson. Had the de Dion firm not voluntarily left the steam wagon field its impact, already considerable, would have been much greater. It left some half-dozen protagonists - Le Blant, whose attempts to establish the road train as a commercial proposition was soon to falter and peter out; Scotte, the Maconnais hatter, whose actual patronym before he changed it to Scotte was Crotte (anglice 'dung' or worse); Weidknecht, mainly interested in buses; Turgan, who produced some interesting heavy vehicles; Chaboche, who built steam vans in the one to two ton class; and Valentin Purrey, who made the only sustained and successful attempt to market steam lorries. Serpollet, as already noted, was mainly interested in cars and rail-mounted vehicles. Had he lived longer his influence on steam wagon design might have been greater, but he died in 1907, and though his influence lingered on in the firm of Darracq-Serpollet who were responsible for the steam buses in the *Metropolitan* fleet, the combination of the absence of Serpollet's engineering genius and the presence of Darracq's personal and financial eccentricities brought the company to its downfall. The Turgan vehicles, made by Turgan, Foy & Cie. at Levallois-Perret, started with cars c.1899, progressed to steam buses, and ended with 3 and 6-ton steam wagons using a double drum water-tube boiler and separate compound engines for each rear wheel. Their interest in steam vehicles flagged about 1905. Scotte, who, following Crompton's experience with the Thomson road steamers, preferred a vertical boiler with Field tubes, used a compound marine type vertical engine. Like Le Blant and Serpollet he had already been in the field by the early 90's but sales of his vehicles were in decline by 1905 and the last recorded, a Red Cross ambulance train, appeared in 1909.

These departures left Valentin Purrey as the only active steam wagon builder in France, and certainly founder of the longest lived marque. Between 1898 and 1929, (the beginning and end of wagon building, respectively) the firm was carried on successively by Purrey, then (1908-13) by Purrey & Exshaw, and finally by H.Exshaw & Co. It is still in business in general engineering in Bordeaux. Purrey wagons were used in the carting of spoil arising from the construction of the Paris Metro; by the Say sugar refinery in Paris, who, even in 1906, had sixteen 10-ton Purreys; and by the Paris municipal authorities for use in street cleaning and gully emptying. Purreys also saw service with the French Army as well as with numerous gas companies and commercial operators. The Purrey boiler was a dry-backed water-tube type

Fig.67. *Clarkson 3-ton wagon used as a service lorry between Moulsham Works, Chelmsford, and the National Steam Car Co.Ltd.'s London garages. Built in 1911 with paraffin firing, it was converted in 1913 to burn coke, and in 1917, because of the wartime shortage of vehicles, it was given a bus body.*

Fig. 68. *One of a fleet of 50 Purrey wagons on hire to Le Petit Parisien.*
Fig.69. *A Lalonde Bros.& Parham Fowler with loads.* (W.S.Love collection)

and the engine, initially compound, was latterly simple expansion. So far as is known all Purreys were single speed. Despite the long period of production it has been estimated that the total Purrey output was about 250 wagons - not many in relation to the total number of heavy vehicles in France. Indeed de Dion had sold more heavy steamers and buses. France had been the first into steam wagons and the first out.

The United States was also early into steam haulage with the big Best three-wheeled haulage engines in California, which have already been discussed, but did not begin to build steam wagons until the turn of the century and then only on a very tentative basis. The Morgan, built in Worcester, Massachusetts, using a very elaborate, and correspondingly expensive, water-tube boiler fired on crude oil, on the scanty evidence available, seems to have been an American production of the Lifu. Another wagon of that period was the Cunningham made in 1900 and 1901 in Boston. This had a conventional coal or coke fired fire-tube boiler and was said to have been chain driven on to all four wheels from a central underfloor engine. How this functioned on the steered axle requires a little working out, and surviving pictures do not make the suggestion very convincing.

Soon after these two oddities the Michigan, the longest lasting American steam lorry, came onto the market. This was built by the Michigan Steam Motor Co. in Detroit from 1902 until about 1914. Like the Purrey in France, Michigan offered load capacities up to 10 tons, though the range included also a 1-tonner and a 3-tonner. The steam was supplied at 350 p.s.i. from a Stanley-type wire wound vertical fire-tube boiler fired with the lighter fraction oils. Since the boiler was situated under the driver's seat this must have made an already uncomfortable position truly hazardous. A condenser was placed in the conventional radiator position. Drive was by propellor shaft to a countershaft differential and thence by two roller chains. What made the Michigan truly remarkable, however, was the V-engine, containing in each arm of the vee, one high pressure, two intermediate pressure, and one low pressure cylinder. This engine was placed under a short bonnet. Artillery wheels on solid rubbers completed what must have been a notable vehicle. The same features that made it notable were also its undoing. In a country almost awash with cheap petrol its sophisticated engine arrangements made it dear to build and maintain, leaving it susceptible to the competition of the available large and simple, even if wasteful, petrol engines. During the period when the Michigan was in production long-distance mechanical road haulage was not practical in North America. Trunking began only in 1917, several years after it had commenced in Great Britain, when the Goodyear Company started running from Akron (Ohio) to Boston (Massachusetts) with 5-ton Packard trucks.

Three unrelated factors spurred the beginning of long-distance road transport in this country. The first was the existence of a comprehensive network of roads which, even after allowing for the disabilities considered in Chapters 1 and 2, were much in advance of what was available outside city limits in the United States and Canada. This provided the means. The second was the restricted loading gauge on the railways. In the first decade of this century this made an increasing number of articles of commerce out-of-gauge loads for rail transport. The burgeoning of the public electricity supply industry, for instance, had led to many indivisible items being required in places which industry had previously passed by. Again, the increasing sophistication of coal gas-making plant had also stretched rail transport to the limits. The third factor was the rough handling that household effects and other more fragile items received when dispatched by rail in goods trains, To avoid this a furniture remover would often have his pantechnicons loaded onto carriage trucks for conveyance by passenger trains, an expensive method. Consequently furniture removers became very interested experimenters with steam haulage on the road over longer distances.

Without making any claims as to who was first in this latter field, it is safe to say that Lalonde Brothers & Parham of Weston-super-Mare were among the pioneers, using Fowler road locomotives and vans. It was Lalonde who complained at an early meeting of The National Traction Engine Owners Association of which, by the way, he was a founder member and enthusiastic supporter, that one of his engines had been stopped in Weston for travelling after sunset. When he had halted it on the roadside for the night as he was entitled to do, provided it had lamps burning, he had been promptly charged with parking the vans on the highway.

The Lalonde fleet was interesting, though it never had more than four engines at a time. The first one they owned was an Aveling & Porter single cylinder (No.3042 of 1892) which they sold to J.& A.H.Murch, the threshing contractors of Umberleigh, Devon. How long Lalondes had it is not known but it was with the Murch family by 1900. The next purchases were two Fowler A4 compounds, Nos.7108 (July, 1894) and 7214 (December, 1894), which in turn were replaced by a pair of A5 compounds (Nos.9382, October, 1902, and 9384, February, 1904), supplemented in March, 1905, by two more (9388 and 9393). There followed their difference of opinion with Fowlers. Lalondes wanted some variations to Fowlers' standard design which the Steam Plough Works, flush with an unprecedented demand for steam ploughing engines for export, either would not or could not supply. Instead Lalondes turned to Richard Garrett & Sons Ltd. for a 6NHP road locomotive (No.26695 of March, 1908) designed with their requirements in view. This turned out to be so great a disappointment to them that the incident ended in a settlement between the lawyers of the respective firms. By 1912, Lalondes had reconciled themselves to Fowlers who had, in the meantime, designed the R3 locomotive with the furniture removing trade in mind. The example Lalondes bought was No.12265, delivered in February, 1912. This subsequently had a second career converted to a showman's engine for T.Teago of Caernarvon, a fate shared by No.9393, which went to Anderton & Haslam at Plymouth in 1921. It is reputed that Lalondes had been the owners at one time of a Burrell locomotive also. About 1904/05 they had begun the experimental use of a steam wagon of unknown provenance. This pioneer lasted until 1913. It was supplemented by a Foden 5-tonner (No.2526, 1911) and a Sentinel 6-tonner (No.619) and when these came up for replacement early in the twenties they had two Foden 5-tonners, (9016 of 1919, and 9654, 1920) and a 3-ton Foden No.10520 (1921). This last was used until 1930 but the two 5-tonners were sold in 1927 and 1929 respectively.

Whilst your author was on the editorial panel of the now defunct (and lamented) magazine *Old Motor*, Mr E.Thorpe of the firm of Richard Thorpe of Ripon,Yorkshire, contributed some reminiscences of his early days in the business when, as a trailer boy, it was his duty to ride on one of the vans to work the brakes. A string ran from his position to the steersman's arm. A tug meant that some other vehicle wanted to pass. Repeated tugs meant that something was wrong at the back - perhaps an overheated wheel bush. Mr. Thorpe began work at the age of fourteen in 1910. His reminiscences are an interesting commentary on the trade at the time:

> "Normally one progressed on the crown of the road, the reason being that the highways consisted of local stone and earth rolled together and waterbound, with a very sharp camber to drain surface water into 'grips' dug at intervals at the roadside. In wet weather this camber made it difficult to avoid skidding off the road with steel-shod wheels.
>
> First promotion was to steersman - the driver had a full-time job looking after the motive power - and one now got out of most of the dust, smoke and cinders, but was faced with the greater responsibility of keeping the whole outfit on the road, not an easy task with steering by worm-wheel, roller and chain. Although the chains were fitted with stout coil springs at one end to take up the shock of snatch, any road surface irregularity combined with a lapse of steering concentration would cause the steering wheel to spin sharply and administer a sharp rap on the back of the hand. Another part of the training was to get up in the morning an hour before anyone else to sweep the boiler tubes, clean out the firebars and ashpan and fill the feed-water tank from the garage tap. At homebase, while the fire was burning up, the bunker would be filled, but when away on a journey a further task was to clean up all signs of a visit. After a period as steersman, oiling of the various mechanisms would be added to the tasks just mentioned. In due course one would be allowed to move the wagon under supervision. Eventually the time came for me to receive a licence. I obtained mine in 1912, but was not allowed to drive regularly until 1913.
>
> The business was founded by my grandfather, in 1868, who passed it on to my father in 1895. At this time the horse was still the prime mover, and our work was mainly local haulage and removals. All removals over 60 miles were undertaken by rail, although on occasions horses were sent to Bridlington and all over the Dales. However, my father, a restless man, was forever on the watch for something more efficient than horseflesh. His first experiment in mechanical transport was to hire a Fowler traction engine, *Doris* (No.9171), from a Mr.A.Atkinson, to carry out a removal from Ripon to Scarborough. This trip was fairly successful and the engine was used on several occasions. It was realised, however, that this big engine was somewhat heavy and cumbersome for furniture work, so my father cast about for something more suitable. At the time steam wagon manufacturers were prepared to hire out vehicles, plus driver, for trial runs, and arrangements were accordingly made with the Yorkshire firm at Leeds to carry out a removal to Carnforth. As a result of such experiments, a Foden 5-tonner was eventually purchased in 1909. This gave yeoman service and travelled over most of the country in its time.
>
> One of the first long-distance runs made by this Foden was from Ripon to Slough, with a van and open trailer, all on steel wheels. A return load for Ripon, consisting of five tons of stack sheeting, was obtained from London Docks, and it is believed that this was the first return load brought by road from London to Yorkshire. I took this wagon to many places in Lancashire, Yorkshire, and Northumberland, until October, 1914, when I was instructed to take it by road to Amesbury, Wilts, to work on the building of camps for the Canadians."

Heelas, owners of the Reading furniture store, were also active in promoting household removals by road, using their own vans hauled by engines hired from Charles Openshaw of the same town. Openshaw was not only well-known as a haulage contractor with an exceptionally well kept stud of road locomotives but also as a repairer and converter of engines. In effect these firms were doing in a relatively sophisticated way what had often been done in a makeshift fashion by local traction engine

Fig.70. Fowler 9971, Doris, *hauling for Richard Thorpe of Ripon who stands in the white apron at the front of the leading van with H.Cuthbert, Atkinson's driver.*
Fig.71. (below) Ernest Reeves began the use of steam by hiring Wallis & Steevens 5-ton tractor No.7480 from Isaiah Gadd.

Fig.72. (left) There was an obverse side to furniture bumping, as to most trades, demonstrated by Robinson Bros.' (Manchester) driver in the snow beside their 3-ton Foden No.2916 (1912) at Buxton on December 30th, 1913. In 1919 the wagon went to Plymouth Cooperative Society and was scrapped in 1928. It had a low platform and long chassis for carrying lift van bodies and also was fitted with a large back box under the platform.

Fig.73. (right) Norman E.Box's Garrett 4CD No.32680, fitted with Tangent rear wheels shod with solid rubbers, with a bulky and out-of-gauge, though not terribly heavy, load on a fairly crude carrying vehicle, February 9, 1918.

owners when they had piled the contents of a cottage or house onto a couple of farm wagons and hauled them to the next village. Furniture is a bulky rather than a heavy load. Three pantechnicons was an easy load for one of Lalonde's or Openshaw's Fowlers and many households did not require more than two vans to move their effects. This led to an interest in the steam tractor as an adjunct to the furniture bumping trade and, by parallel thinking, as in Lalonde's case, into employment of the rapidly developing steam wagon. When discussing Straker earlier, we noticed Arthur Wedgwood's early involvement with steam furniture haulage on his converted Straker steam bus. William Whiteley, of the Queensway (London) department store, personally one of the more repulsive examples of the self-made man, was brilliant in his business decisions. Ahead of most of his competitors he recognized the potential of the steam wagon for moving furniture and was early in the field with a Thornycroft, though the firm's later steamers came from Fodens. By contrast, Waring & Gillow, West End holders of the Royal Warrant, had a steam van built for them by Edward Gillett of Hounslow, who was mainly concerned with the machinery of small river craft. Gillett's vehicle, an oil-fired undertype with a down-take exhaust and compound undertype engine, in an oil-tight casing integral with the rear axle, was conceived on the lines of an expanded steam car and was undoubtedly an elegant vehicle. It served its owners from 1903 to 1910 which cannot be counted bad for a pioneer but, being essentially an elegant vehicle for carrying light loads in well paved streets, it lacked the rugged durability of the Foden or of the R.A.F. type Leyland petrol engined lorries which the firm subsequently used for many years.

After this early flourish the furniture trade, as a whole, proved fickle toward steam transport. Most removal firms had fled from it by the opening of the twenties though a few remained constant. The firm of E.W.Reeves & Co. of Wokingham with their Sentinel Super (No.5248, December, 1923) were one such. Peace of Bridgwater and Bournemouth were another, with Garrett undertype 8-tonner No.34671 (1924). Curtis of Portsmouth used their Fodens throughout the twenties, and there were other adherents. Not many bothered, however, to convert their steam wagons from solid rubbers to pneumatics which would have reduced breakages and this, taken with changes in the Road Fund taxation in the early thirties, and with the rather better cleanliness obtainable from motors, finally ousted steam from the furniture removal business.

Dock haulage in Liverpool which had been the cradle of the British steam wagon was also one of its last refuges. The Coulthard wagons had laid an early hold, with Lancashires (Leylands) also well in the running. The wagon which figured in the account of a night-time run, published in *Motor Car Journal* for January 3, 1903, appears to have been a Leyland 'B', and the description of the run itself is illuminating as well as entertaining - marred only by the mincing style of the narrative - and is worth quoting at length. Though the identity of the firm involved was not disclosed, Charles Lloyd has suggested it was the Road Carrying Co. who ran to Preston and Blackburn. The starting point was in the Vauxhall Road area of Liverpool.

"It is now 5.30. The in-coming lorries are returning from their day trip to St.Helens and back. Six arrive within thirty-five minutes. Three are to go to Blackburn tonight, but only two of these are yet in. They have on board their loads of cotton from the docks. No, neither of these is my lorry. Where is number eleven? asks Mr.Rosenheim, the engineer, of Foreman Ambler. "Towing in number fourteen," comes the ominous reply, which makes the thirst for copy liven a little. Shortly after, number eleven enters the depot on the low gear, both she and her helpless trailer under full loads. A small connection to one of the pumps had fractured three miles from home. Immediately comes the inspection by the running shed staff, and number eleven is pronounced fit for the night-shift trip to Blackburn. The day driver enters the office to hand in his records, and he of the night has already rung on duty. A reliable and determined-looking man is my judgment, as he goes down to the stores, in the company of his fireman, the two re-appearing almost instantly loaded with two oilskin coats and no less than *six* hurricane lamps. Fourteen bags of coke are certified for, one gallon of engine oil, and sundry oddments. Meantime, number eleven has been backed by one of the depot men to the end of the shed nearest to the departure gate, but without a load. ..... Suddenly the gate is run back, and a waiting horse-drawn lorry is discerned in the street. Sheets fly off, and the vault opens simultaneously - Petrol, by Jove! I exclaim involuntarily, with visions of premature cremation. Was I to ride to Blackburn without a smoke? And what were the odds that the ashpan would not have a share in providing a healthy conflagration? "Reject that case," shouted the foreman loader, and I returned to my wits to see a leaking tin sent back to store by the cart, case and all. Row upon row, some off the cart and some from the vault, were the cases built compactly together. "We like the load, it sits well," was the nonchalant reply to my enquiry as to what the men thought.

In half an hour all was on and double-sheeted. A spar-like pole was erected horizontally at the back, above the load, and the tail lamp secured thereto. "Petrol vapour is heavier than air, and the front lamps are never in it," was the only explanation needed or vouchsafed. Four of the hurricane lamps were suspended at the front of the lorry, and a fifth was placed on the footboard, behind the boiler, to show the gauges.

SEVEN-THIRTY, and we are off! I am ensconced on a sack on the top of the tool-box, between the driver and fireman. The novelty, not to say apprehension, of being on a vehicle carrying eight hundred gallons of petroleum spirit - for that was our load - quickly wore off. The Vauxhall Road Depot, from which we started, lies practically in the centre of

Liverpool, and it was exactly four miles to the Sefton Arms, Aintree, where we plunged into darkness, leaving both tram-lines and dwellings astern. Never shall I forget that plunge. The lorry slowed down from six to about three miles an hour, and my high opinion of the driver gave place to a sense of trepidation. The man was steering by the line of the off-side kerb, or the hedge, where there was no foot-walk, the object of the extra hurricane lamps being apparent as their beams shone out obliquely against the sides of the road. On the near-side the fireman kept watch between his intervals of stoking. Ever and anon he shovelled coke upon the concave top of the boiler casing, where it dried slightly before being dropped down the central shoot by lifting the round lid. He was shovelling and lifting as for dear life, and the engine was pulling hard. To keep 200 lbs. of steam was evidently a tussle. Whilst less than 150 meant low gear. The macadam was shocking. The mud squelched and oozed under the six-inch drivers, which had been tripping gaily when we remained on the excellent Liverpool setts. Suddenly the car jumped forward. We were on setts again, and climbing a canal bridge. Bump, bang, smack go the springs on the stop-blocks, and my liver is already less sluggish. These holes in the road are anguish, but the driver apologetically assures me that he now knows most of them, and avoids them to ensure his bonus for the condition of his wagon.

We are at the *Old Roan Inn,* five miles from the depot and seven times that from our destination. Time occupied, one hour and three minutes. I am informed that the mud and slush on the mile of macadam just traversed is as heavy as anything until we get to Rufford. This is interesting. perhaps we shall stick altogether or go through the crust later on. No, we had not yet been in low gear. The coke is none too good, and quickly forms heavy clinker, in consequence of which we have wasted fuel and steam by having the blast going from the instant we left the setts. I ply the driver with questions, and am quickly reassured as to his ability. The darkness is no longer oppressive, though the rain is pitiless. The 'spark arrestor', a clumsy and cumbersome contrivance of wire gauze, having two layers of 64-mesh to the inch, is removed and stowed away, now that we are in the country. One can readily see how it interferes with the draught on the fire. Clinkering over, watering follows. The suction hose is uncoiled, a lid by the roadside lifted, and the rose dropped, to all intents and purposes, into the ground, I unhitch one of the hurricane lamps to assist inspection, the driver meantime explaining that this is one of the company's watering stations. Serious troubles and difficulties over the taking of water from canals, streams, and troughs have been solved by the putting in of large tanks underground, securely lagged against frost, and kept full by ball-valve regulators. The supply is by meter, and these tanks are stationed at selected points every few miles on the roads served by the wagons. But woe betide the stranger who seeks to help himself, for the local police and residents are on the qui vive to earn the reward which is offered for the detection of any wrongful consumption of the supplies.

Nine o'clock finds us on the road again, prospects being more cheery. We are averaging a mile in eleven minutes - subject to what the driver tells me as to the location of the milestones. Steam is maintained at full pressure, and sparks fly generously enough to cause me to pull down my cap. I watch these sparks; I positively hang my vision on nothing else. Thank goodness they die at once! Two only fall on the sheet in quite a long space of time; the rain and sheets will save my skin. I feel that I could no more get the driver to replace the spark arrestor than I could drive the wagon myself. There is evidently an aversion to them. Leaving Aughton Church on the right, we climb a long hill, barely scraping up on the high gear, and almost run down into Ormskirk without steam. There is reunion at the *Talbot Hotel,* where Nos.1 and 8 are found watering etc., and it is 10.40p.m. as we bring up the rear of a miniature procession past the Clock Tower and along a dangerously narrow street. The men drive hard. It is six miles to supper. The elements appear to favour us, relatively, for the rain ceases and the roads are less heavy. The crust, may be, contains 30% of water against 60 further back; but we must be thankful for small mercies when on iron tyres carrying a total weight of over eight tons. I do not want to say that we cover a mile at eight an hour. All the same, we take only fifty-two minutes to travel the six miles to the *Hesketh Arms,* Rufford, where we arrive some minutes ahead of the cotton lorries. All is darkness, but the men are at home. Their baskets and cans are brought forth, as introductory to an adjournment into a comfortable stable, the key of which is discovered from some hiding-place. There is masonry in the air, but I appear to be a welcome visitor. My sandwiches and a bottle of brandy - brought as a precaution - are partaken of. The 'Pros and Cons' of how far the Blackburn men will get that night are discussed, which reveals the fact that my driver alone is going through, the other two Liverpool drivers having to change when they meet their charges from the other end of the service. This system of relief is being tried as an experiment, the advantage being that each set of men retraverse their own bit of road, and get back to their own homes.

Here is one. A Blackburn man arrives shortly after midnight, his lorry (No.7) snugly packed with four tons of baled cloth for shipment to Calcutta. Not a single trailer is out in this weather, so the loads are small per unit, but forty tons of this shipment is coming forward, spread over three days. My trusty steed, No.11, stands by until one o'clock, while I watch the departure of the other three - two to Blackburn, and one to Liverpool. We have been warned to 'low-gear it' under the trees through Rufford Wood, and get safely through. A mile on, near Sollom, we are in difficulties. The road has become heavier and heavier, we are below the level of the surrounding country, which I am told is a moss, when, with a crunch and a knock, we stop dead. The four-way cock, plus low gear, is futile. We are going down on the near-side wheels. We are turning over, possibly. I dismount with more haste than decorum, into mud over my boot-tops, to gauge the angle of inclination and to look at my watch. It is 1.28a.m., and we are stranded in the wilderness.

"Here's a pretty go, here's a how d'you do!" occurred to me as an appropriate ejaculatory comment on the situation, which feeling was in nowise diminished by the departure of the driver, and fireman, who stolidly informed me they would be back in an hour. I listened meditatively to the tramp of their feet on the cindered sidewalk as they stalked back towards Liverpool for assistance, each swinging a hurricane lamp whose adaptations seemed universal. The lights disappearing round a bend, I turned again to my charge. "Keep an eye on the water-gauge," had been the driver's parting injunction after he had pumped the boiler nearly full and dampened the fire. ....

When the Klinger gauge shows one bare inch, I start the Marsh pump to replenish the boiler, and at least find company in the resonant working of the valves, proving their action by the slowly augmented level in the glass. One and a half mortal hours do I wait for the 'tackle ' to arrive. It comes on a spring cart at three o'clock. Out come the big lifting jacks and packings, and out we come. All over in fifteen minutes, with the aid of a little verbal encouragement, which I need not repeat. The 'tackle' is driven off by hay-motor, back to Rufford, and a delay which might easily have reached a dozen hours is overcome in less than two.

Fig. 74. Yorkshire was not the commonest make on Merseyside. Apart from the Mersey Docks & Harbour Board whose wagon No.4 is shown, the only sizeable fleet was that of the Liverpool Warehousing Co.Ltd. who had 44 of them.

Fig. 75. Atkinson No.37 (1917), shown here when owned by Webster's (Wigan) Ltd., passed to J.Bibby & Sons Ltd. in 1924. After several rebuilds it finally became a tractor on pneumatics, in which form it ran until 1947.

Fig. 76. William Harper & Sons' Sentinel Super No.6258 in traffic in Liverpool in November, 1951, well cleaned by an attentive crew, but its apron bearing the scars of work in the docks. [John H.Meredith]

Fig. 77. J.Bibby & Sons' Garrett superheated 5-tonner No.32704, which they had in 1915.

We are in low gear for the next mile, then change to high and keep there, moving nicely. The road is apparently fit to admit the use of that designation, and allows our making up for evil times. We drop anchor, or rather stop to uncoil the watering hose, at the *Bridge Inn*, Penwortham, with the lights of Preston dancing on the waters of the Ribble, the whole forming an enticing contrast to the twenty-six miles of road through which we have toiled, at 4.47a.m. ....

We have slackened to three miles an hour on the setts, to reduce the noise and vibration. We approach Brockholes Brow, the steep descent to the Ribble on the new Preston-Blackburn road. I recollect the grade as 1 in 13, from the profiles of the Liverpool Trials routes. The surface is ghastly, yet we do manage to keep moving, being down hill, by giving her full steam. They evidently believe in sand as a binding material hereabouts, without anything to bind unless it be the traffic. The road is nothing short of a crying disgrace, which would not be tolerated in the South. We jog along, notwithstanding, and reach the *Five Barred Gate*, Samlesbury, at 6.30a.m., this being about five miles from home and the last watering station. The men here accept their second 'refresher' at my hands, and earn my golden opinions by their abstemious conduct.

Incidents cease. We reach Simmons Street, Sudell Cross, a little before eight, fit and well. The depot here is a disused tram-way shed, into which the Vauxhall Road establishment could be fitted twice. No.11 is taken over by the running-shed men, and I take my departure to the *Old Bull Hotel*, where the landlord, Mr.H.Burton Berry, had been notified of my requirements and prepared right royally. By nine o'clock I am snugly between the sheets, with a roaring fire and curtains drawn, dreaming of mud, of ditches, of hedges, and of having accomplished forty miles in twelve hours."

Aside from the general interest of the passage it is arresting both as a reminder of how steam wagon haulage had established itself in the bare seven years since it had become legal and the illustration of the extent of the infra-structure it had built up. In 1896 nothing was on offer beyond the Thornycroft steam van. By 1903 the steam wagon had become an everyday tool of work backed up by the established depots, prearranged water points, and organised maintenance and traffic.

Steam was never absent from the Liverpool Docks from that time until the outset of the sixties when the last of the United Africa wagons was laid off. The oilseed trade - Simmonds; Hunt & Montgomery; Silcocks; Bibbys; and Criddles - were staunch employers of steam as were the sugar refiners Fairries, with their Leylands, and, later, Tate & Lyle. The flour millers and traders were active users of Sentinels - W.G.Vernon & Sons Ltd.; Benjamin Sykes & Sons Ltd; and White Tomkins & Courage Ltd - though Woods of Birtwistle used Fodens. The general dock hauliers such as Websters; Davies; Kirkdale Haulage; and Bennetts who were steam to the end, which in Bennetts' case meant nationalisation, were also mostly Sentinel users. One of the sights of the nineteen-fifties in Liverpool was to encounter one of the forty year old Standard Sentinels of Kirkdale Haulage, gaunt, battered, with open fronted cab, lit after dark by a pair of hurricane lamps, yet still doing the work it had been built for. In the early days Coulthards' products, from Preston, were numerous as were Leylands and, at the end of the 1914-18 war, Atkinsons. Fodens were much in evidence, though more from firms running into Liverpool than from owners within the city itself, who remained fairly solidly in favour of the undertype. The overtype Garrett had a foothold in the Lancashire cotton trade and was to be seen in Liverpool, but the make of wagon with the greatest hold on the loyalties of Liverpool haulage firms was the Sentinel, of the Standard, Super, or DG types but less often the S-type. The Sentinel was backed up by the almost legendary Sentinel Service Depot run by Jimmy Stott in Vauxhall Road. Whether the popularity of the Sentinel begat Stott, or Stott's efficiency helped to sell Sentinels is hardly knowable, but the fact of the depot's existence must have prolonged the life of Sentinels in Liverpool. Sick wagons would limp into it at the end of a day's work and be ready for the road again the next morning.

The conditions of dock work were punishing. Roadways within the docks were rough, frequently of granite setts, and intersected by railway lines. The approaches to and exits from loading points often involved short, very steep slopes and Liverpool dockers were noted for their militancy (with a small 'm') and for their cavalier attitude to hauliers' wagons. All these points added up to a rough life for the latter which probably accounts for the late survival of Standards, Supers, and DG's rather than S-types. When the front apron of a Standard received a contusion it could be put back more or less into workable shape with no more sophisticated equipment than a couple of big hammers but damage to the superior cab of an S-type probably required the attention of a body-builder. Hogged frames, broken springs, and racked bodywork were the hazards of dock service but many wagons survived them for thirty years or more to pass ultimately into preservation.

The wagons and their conditions of work produced a sprinkling of notable characters amongst drivers, some remembered with affection, others simply seared onto the memory. Cocky Roberts who drove a Standard for Woods, falls into the former class as George Lea recalls:

"Coming down into Warrington from Northwich the driving chain broke and in no time at all the outfit was really away. Cocky stuck to the wheel, frantically blowing the horn, and both he and his mate shouted their heads off to move people off the road. They swept through Stockton Heath passing other vehicles; then, as they approached the swing bridge the queue which was waiting, due to the gates being closed, had graciously kept the offside of the road clear. Onlookers later described it as 'doing well over sixty' and 'being just a blur'.

At the gates there is a cross-road and Cocky tried to pull round to the right but could not make it owing to his speed and the waiting traffic on this road. So he had no alternative than to go through the railings, to topple over and slide down the embankment, coming to rest at the side of the canal. Cocky died later from the burns and scalds he received in an act of gallantry that caused injury to none save himself, and no damage to property beyond that to the railings and the wagon."

Not every runaway ended in tragedy. The same mishap, i.e. the breaking of the chain, befell the Foden 4-tonner (No.6468) owned by Browns of Wilmslow. Returning from Buxton with a load of lime the crew had the misfortune to have the chain part on a downhill stretch by the *Setter Dog* at Walker Barn. The wagon brake and the trailer brake were screwed hard on and the driver (Bill) steered in the gutter but the wagon would not stop. George Lea's account of the incident goes on:

"They came out into the road again and Bill's mate jumped off - it must be realised that they were not screaming along; it was just that they could not come to a halt - so he screwed down the hand wheel on the trailer, then began to throw lumps of lime under the wheels to try and scotch them. But it was all to no avail. Bill was now getting worried as they were then approaching the steeper descent down into Macclesfield. There was only one course left open, which was to rub along the stone wall, and this did bring them to a halt without serious damage, beyond a few scars and displaced stones."

Both these accidents resulted from the fact that the brakes unaided were incapable of stopping the wagon, leading to reliance on the reversing lever and hence the engine as a supplement. Once the chain had parted there was no retarding effect from the engine, and the runaway was unavoidable. In each case the brakes were open bands, liable to contamination with oil which decreased their usefulness. Wagons were habitually overloaded by anything up to 100% which aggravated matters. It must not be imagined that steam vehicles were unique in the poverty of their braking. Indeed, apart from the mischance of breakage of the chain, they were a great deal better off in this respect than many motor lorries of the twenties.

In London, the emphasis was much less on the oil seed trade, but the flour millers, who frequently took their grain in from wharves served by barges or lighters, were extensive users of steam wagons for distribution until the change in the basis of taxation in 1933. Hovis Ltd, from their mill by Vauxhall Bridge, used a fleet of undertypes, made up for some years of Garretts, but in its final phase, of DG Sentinels, whilst Joseph Rank used Fodens to serve their mill at Victoria Docks. Fodens had also been prominent in the rolling stock of other London area millers - Mark Mayhew at Battersea; the Sun Flour Mills at Bow; Fountains at Uxbridge; J.& H.Robinson of Deptford; Samuel Kidd of Isleworth. The chilled and frozen meat run from the East and West India Docks to Smithfield Market employed steam wagons, in the use of which E.W.Rudd was a pioneer. Rudd's earliest wagons were Coulthards but to replace them he went to the overtype, choosing the Garrett in the design of which he had had a voice, through his friendly relationship with Frank Garrett Senior. Rudd's wagons in those days were painted blue with red wheels. Because they were well looked after and the fleet was turned over relatively rapidly second-hand Rudd wagons were popular on fairgrounds. Rudd moved from steam to motors in the early twenties though he retained steam, in the shape of Fowler road locomotive No.14291, until the late thirties for heavy haulage purposes, but other firms in the meat haulage business such as Faircloughs, Union Cartage, Cornells, and Matthews, went on using steam for much longer, cutting their wagons down to tractors in the 30's to avoid the penal taxation on wagons that followed the Salter Report. A few of these tractors outlasted the second world war.

The trade from upriver wharves and hards served by lighters and barges engaged a great variety - perhaps a ragged assembly - of wagons usually over short distances. Fodens were dominant but other overtypes - Strakers, Clayton & Shuttleworths, Garretts, and Avelings - were represented. Manns were relatively rare but Beck & Pollitzer, the machinery movers and exhibition specialists with a depot in Lambeth, had a small fleet of them, smartly turned out. Among the general hauliers along the Thames who used Fodens were Thomas Feast of Silvertown; T.Mileham & Sons of Canning Town; Hays Wharf Cartage Co., who also carried meat; George Painter & Sons, and E.Wells & Sons Ltd., both of Rotherhithe; Charles Poulter Ltd. of Stepney; Yorke Stoneham & Jones; and A.E.Gains. Yorke Stoneham & Jones wagons were to be seen almost at water level on the Thames-side hards being loaded direct over the sides of barges or lighters. Eastwoods, the builders' merchants, had three barges engaged in bringing red facing bricks from the brickyard at Aldeburgh alone to the up-river discharge points.

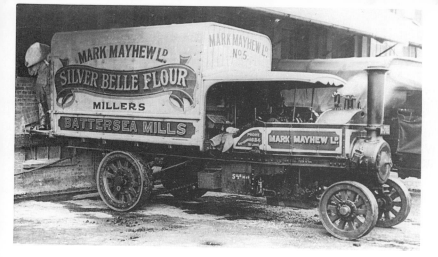

Fig.78. London flour millers were prominent users of steam wagons. Yhis is Foden No.1439 (1907) which was wagon No.5 in the fleet of Mark Mayhew Ltd. at Battersea.

Fig.79. The final wagons used by flour mills in London were mainly Sentinels. This is Sentinel DG 6, No.7163 (1928) in the fleet of Hovis Ltd. in Pimlico.

Fig.80. Fodens in the Smithfield meat trade included No.5014 of 1915 seen here in Charterhouse Square in the ownership of R.Cornell Ltd., the Smithfield carriers. The trailer is a former horse-drawn van.

Fig.81. Many wagons in the London wholesale meat trade ended up as tractors, as did Foden No.10864 (1922) seen by Derek Stoyel at Kingston-upon-Thames in April, 1936.

Another aspect of river traffic in which wagons were involved was the builders' 'rubbish away' trade in which the debris and leavings of building operations in the parts of the Metropolis readily accessible from Thames-side or its associated creeks and canals were loaded into barges for disposal on the down-river marshes. St.Mary's Wharves at Paddington were used for such tipping, as were the truncated Grosvenor Canal near Victoria Station; Willment's Wharf at Waterloo; Murrells Wharf; the wharves off Sullivan Road, Fulham; Horace Cunis's Wharf at Limehouse; the wharves flanking Deptford Creek and Chelsea Creek; and many more. Nearly all the debris was loaded on to the wagons by hand over the side but major contracts on which a crane was installed often had skips or an overhead hopper. Firms running in sand and ballast from the Middlesex or Hertfordshire pits gladly took return loads for tipping in the spent areas of their workings. St.Albans Sand & Gravel very largely back-filled their pit at London Colney in this way. Firms like Herts Gravel & Brickworks; Willment Bros; Bettles & Box; Sand & Shingle Ltd; E.J.Mylon; and Mylon Bros. all took part in this trade.

The cement trade from the Thames and the Medway to London depended heavily on barge traffic. The biggest users were the Cement Marketing Co. Ltd, formed by the merging of most of the major down-river producers, though their hopes of creating a total monopoly were destroyed by the setting up of the Danish controlled Tunnel Cement Co. at Grays on the Thames, and the Rugby Portland Cement Co. at Snodland on the Medway. From the first, Tunnel distributed by road using Sentinel 6-wheelers on contract hire from C.Durston Ltd. The C.M.C. distribution, under their trade mark *Blue Circle*, was done from riverside depots by the famous fleet of yellow Sentinels, mainly DG's, both four and six-wheeled. Blue Circle were one of the few users who made a determined effort to stay with steam after 1934 and added some S-type wagons to their fleet, which was not finally denuded of steam until the late nineteen-forties.

London steam wagons underwent a dreadful carnage in 1933-34 but some firms, perhaps more thoughtful than their competitors, followed the example of the Smithfield carriers and went in for tractors. Thus Beck & Pollitzer continued to use Fodens Nos. 12770 (1928) and 13090 (built in 1928 but sold in 1934), and they were kept going until after the war. On the other hand, the St.Mary's Wharf Cartage Co. Ltd. fleet of 6-wheeled Sentinels used on hauling away the excavated material from the construction of the Piccadilly Line extension to Cockfosters (Middlesex), were all scrapped at the completion of the contract. They had been used day and night during the work with double, or sometimes triple manning, the crews being on piecework. The material was mostly removed to a tip north of Enfield, though some proportion went to South's flower pot factory in Tottenham, the owner of which, by a curious coincidence, was from Leiston, home of Garrett wagons. Residents in Enfield became accustomed, even if not reconciled, to the Sentinels being driven hard through the town. The maxim of the drivers appears to have been "wherever possible, flat out". It has been suggested that the constant thrashing of the wagons meant that they were in poor condition at the end of the contract and thus speeded their demise, but the late Leslie Flack, of St.Mary's, once told the writer that the wagons were in serviceable condition even at the end but simply priced off the road by the rate of taxation which came into force in 1934.

As the weights that heavy hauliers were called upon to transport increased they undoubtedly developed considerable resourcefulness to match these demands, though the journeys were mostly either local or short distance. So far as very heavy items were concerned the railways also displayed resource, culminating in the inter-war years with the London & North Eastern Railway's set of cantilever wagons able to carry a single item weighing up to 150 tons. In order, from the leading end, the set was made up of a 20 ton trolley wagon carrying the balance weight box at the front, followed by a 60 ton twelve wheeled flat wagon to support the cantilever at the leading end. After this came a Weltrol 24-wheeled wagon, 83ft. 2in. in length, on which the actual load reposed. Another 60 ton wagon and a 20 ton trolley wagon completed the outfit, repeating the leading end i.e. with the weight box at the back. The two 60 ton wagons and the 110 ton wagon were coupled with special drawbars to make a composite vehicle 226ft. 2in long. The railways performed some notable feats in moving out-of-gauge items, such as ships' propellors or rudders, which presented rather more problems. They were, of course, at their best in handling loads where both the originating and receiving firms had rail sidings, but the routing of them was, however, extremely difficult. For example when Battersea Power Station was built it utilised a Metropolitan Vickers generator which, at the time, was the largest in Europe. This was moved 284 miles, by rail, from Trafford Park, Manchester, to the site at Battersea on two successive weekends. The problem was not so much the weight, which was no more than 42 tons, or the length (24 ft.4in.) but in the width of 12ft.6in. and the height of 11ft.4in. The route was surveyed with great thoroughness and in some instances the clearances came down to less than an inch. Wolverhampton Tunnel proved an impossible obstacle and consequently the cavalcade was sent over a 42 mile diversion via Kidderminster, Worcester, Evesham, and Stratford-on-Avon to avoid it. To confirm the survey, and to check clearances, a coach fitted with profiles to match the proposed load was taken over the route in a special working. The first weekend the generator reached Old Oak Common, London, only some ten miles from its destination. The next Sunday it was taken over the West London line to South Lambeth. To give sufficient clearance the track had to be slewed at Addison Road. Gangs of platelayers waited to bring it back to its alignment as soon as the special train had passed. Technically the operation was a complete success but it was, as can be imagined, very expensive.

Consequently, as heavy hauliers on the road developed the ability to handle increasingly heavy loads and severely out-of-gauge articles over longer distances they became competitive with the railways. In the matter of loading gauge roads were nearly as vulnerable as railways because of the low over-bridges and overhanging buildings and the presence of such obstacles as telephone lines or tramway overhead. On total weight they were also vulnerable by reason of restricted bridges and culverts, which have already been discussed, and from shallow drains, sewers, and service mains. However, the road haulier had the advantage, marginal at times but sometimes crucial, of being able to vary the position of his vehicle upon the road or even, by plating under the wheels and the use of water or soft-soap as a lubricant, of being able to pull it bodily sideways or through a right angle.

From the position of moving heavy items from one end of a city to another, moving them from factory to waterside, as in Glasgow, or moving them the final short distance from the nearest rail terminal to ultimate destination the heavy hauliers had reached out on ever longer journeys. The following account, culled by John Hirons from various issues of the *Oxford Times* of July and August, 1905, shows that not all journeys were without untoward events and that the carrying vehicles were often inadequate for long distances. The problem of over-restricted bridges was one which plagued road hauliers in general for many years as we have seen, but otherwise most of the other troubles in this account appear from the text to have been of the contractor's own making:

"Two large Scotch marine boilers intended with eight others for use in a first-class battleship being laid down in Portsmouth dockyard were being conveyed on special boiler trolleys hauled by locomotives ...... from Oldbury where they had been constructed by Messrs. William Danks & Co.

The combined weight of each boiler and trolley was about 25 tons apart from the heavy locomotive attached to each for haulage purposes. The drivers stayed on Wednesday night at Sandford, having taken seven days for the journey of 70 miles from Oldbury, and continued their journey at 9a.m. on Thursday morning. The first engine negotiated the short hill by the inn successfully, but the rear engine was less fortunate.

Taking the right-hand side of the road, the boiler trolley passed over the 24in. iron main carrying the sewage from the pumping station at Sandford to the Oxford Corporation farms east of the Sandford Road. The road, unable to bear the strain, gave way and the main was crushed .... The sewage burst out upon the road, carrying away the surface and leaving it like a shingle beach. Down the hill it flowed, forming a pond several inches deep at the bottom. The surface drains were unable to cope with the sudden outburst with the result that the sewage gravitated through the drains into the cottages in the neighbourhood.

An additional complication was that the employees of Oxford Corporation - including the Chief Engineer - were away on their annual outing. So under the supervision of the Mayor, the Estates Surveyor and members of the Engineer's Department, a break-down gang was improvised and the salvage operation began. The road was in the meanwhile closed to traffic and the G.P.O. were informed of the state of affairs in order that the Oxford-London mail coach might not be delayed by getting into a cul-de-sac."

Two weeks later the story continues: "The remainder of the journey was by no means uneventful, for a few days ago the wheels of one of the trolleys sank through the surface of the road at Petersfield and defied the efforts of three traction engines to remove it ..... It does not appear so far that the two first engines intended for Portsmouth have reached their destination.

Numbers three and four which left Oldbury a fortnight ago have experienced even worse fate. With the exception of the normal abrasion of the road all went well until within a few miles of Long Compton, where one of the wheels of a trolley collapsed, necessitating a delay of five days. A fresh start was made but just before reaching Long Compton Hill another wheel collapsed and as far as we know that is as far as the third boiler has got. Boiler No.4 took eight hours to climb Long Compton Hill and arrived at Yarnton on Monday morning.

The Great Western Railway authorities heard of the approach of the 25-ton boiler and immediately took action which resulted in the 'holding up' of the locomotive and its charge on the rise approaching the railway bridge. The drivers, who had not seen a bed for three weeks, decided to await further instructions and a camp was pitched on the side of the road between the boiler and the bridge while the employees of the G.W.R. watched the proceedings day and night to see that the load was not taken on to the bridge.

As the Admiralty have issued strict orders that neither the boiler nor its tractor are to leave the road the space for traffic on the north side of the railway is strictly limited. On Thursday the drivers were still awaiting instructions. We understand that altogether 22 boilers are to be transported by road - for the railway companies will not take them - ten to

Portsmouth and twelve to Chatham, and the ten Portsmouth boilers are to be delivered within ten weeks. At present it looks as if it will be nearer ten months."

The *Oxford Times* continues: "On August 1 Edwin Russell, traction engine driver, of Farnham, Surrey, appeared before Woodstock Magistrates for obstructing the free passage of the highway, when P.C. Hampton gave evidence that the off-wheel straddled the centre of the 21 foot wide road. Then the case was adjourned for a fortnight to allow Russell to communicate with his master with reference to leave he had received that morning from the railway company to pass over the bridge at his own risk. But on August 15 the boiler was still there and he was fined £1.0.0 and 3s.6d. costs with 14 days hard labour in default."

Whether he paid or not the *Oxford Times* does not say. But on September 9 it carried a story which makes the fate of the boiler clear. "No arrangement having been made by the contractors to have the Yarnton Bridge strengthened it was agreed to turn the engine and boiler on August 29 and retraverse the Woodstock Road to Kidlington Station .... While crossing the goods yard the boiler unfortunately got embedded in the ballast (the pathway having been relaid the previous Tuesday), but with the use of three jacks and careful manipulation it was safely placed ready for loading on a special wagon.

From there it was conveyed by rail to Oxford on September 21 where it was stabled with the one put on rail at Chipping Norton and stranded at Long Compton Hill to await four others from Oldbury to which they were attached."

Whilst one can understand that the Corporation of Oxford had just cause for irritation at the crushing of its sewer, it is difficult to see what the contractors could have done to merit such obstruction beyond having attempted something not done before in the district. The railway stance was fairly typical of the period. Despite having no real desire for the out-of-gauge loads themselves they nevertheless wished to obstruct their haulage by road.

Much of the increasing amount of heavy haulage work done by steam traction arose from the immense growth in the use of electricity between the eighteen-nineties and the second world war. Initially there was the setting up of electricity generating works in the major cities and towns. Because early supplies were generally by direct current systems, the effective distance between the point of generation and the furthest user was limited to a matter of four or five miles. Consequently, most undertakings were very local and proportionately small. The electricity requirements of a town of three or four thousand inhabitants were modest and the generating plant needed to satisfy them was sized in proportion. In the major centres of population the demand, even in the opening decade of the century, required a large generating installation and, in many instances, soon needed increases in capacity after demand had expanded and overtaken the capabilities of the original works.

Colonel R.E.B. Crompton, who had made his mark on steam road vehicles in the seventies, was, in the nineteen-hundreds, a prominent figure in the construction and equipping of electricity generating works. With his friend, C. Stanley Peach, the London architect, he was responsible for the design of many power stations. The fact that Col. Crompton was so emphatic in his predisposition toward road transport gave a tremendous boost to the use of steam road haulage for moving heavy plant. Not only did he encourage this on projects for which he was directly responsible but also, by his prestige, led other engineers to look in the same direction. Though the two Glasgow firms of Road Steam Engines, and William Kerr were primarily concerned with the heavy haulage requirements of the Clyde conurbation, Kerrs responded to the opportunities thus provided by undertaking work further afield. Coupe Bros. of Sheffield, well established in their own territory, also took loads for more distant destinations. In London E.W. Rudd; X.Y.Z. Transport of Fulham (Dick Bateman's firm); the London Traction Haulage Co., based in Holmes Road, NW 2; and Coulson & Co. Ltd. of Park Royal all undertook the haulage of large indivisible loads as did Hickey & Sons, the boiler makers and dealers, of Richmond, Surrey. Robert Wynn & Sons, in Newport, South Wales, began steam haulage a little later but became well-known in their area and beyond. Probably the best known heavy haulage firm in England was the Manchester based Norman E. Box Ltd. A major haulage operation by Box was undertaken like a military exercise. Every part of the route to be taken was surveyed in advance, bridge clearances were checked, arrangements were made for removing street furniture or lifting overhead obstructions, and optimum passing times were worked out. As loads grew bigger the degree of pre-planning increased.

Heavy haulage by steam on the road reached its zenith in the twenties and thirties, largely through the improvement in the carrying vehicles. The trade had begun with what were little more than, at best, developed versions of the boiler maker's trolley, large and very strong but crude platform trucks carried either on extremely stoutly made wooden wheels or steel or cast iron wheels broad in the width at the tyres and, proportionately, small in diameter. Most were simply bogies with no steering lock. Such vehicles may have been sufficient for short hauls over the hard pavings of city streets but they imposed heavy point loads, were liable as in the case of the Sandford pumping main to damage shallow pipes,

Fig.82. Wagon No.12 in Beck & Pollitzer's fleet was Mann No.1438.

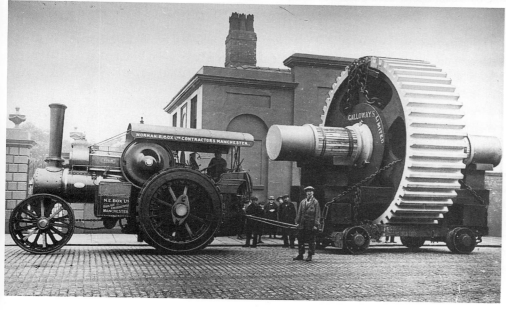

Fig.83. (above) Steam haulage in Glasgow from the 1870's until about 1932 saw the extensive use of the fleet of Thomson road steamers owned by Road Steam Engines Ltd.

Fig. 84. Norman E.Box's Fowler Titan with a 46 ton gear in Manchester in July, 1919. The carrying vehicle is very strong but appallingly crude.

were difficult to steer, and ran heavily. On macadam roads outside towns they were prone to sinking into the softer road crusts and contractors often had to resort to plating, i.e. placing heavy steel plates on the road prior to the passage of the wheels and lifting them and moving forward after they had passed. This was back breaking for the men and agonisingly slow.

Significant improvement was achieved with the introduction of multiwheeled trailers, cambering axles, and solid rubber tyres. In 1927 Pickfords' heavy haulage section, which had taken over the London Traction Haulage Co., put into service an articulated low loader on solid rubbers. This was soon followed by Norman Box's 100-tonner and by Pickfords with a trailer of 160 tons capacity on 32 wheels each on twin solids. R.A.Dyson & Co. Ltd. of Grafton Street, Liverpool; Cranes (Dereham) Ltd, of Dereham, Norfolk; and John Fowler were the most significant contributors to the improvement of carrying vehicles responding to demands from the leading haulage firms. The Dyson 75 ton trailer delivered to Road Engines & Kerr (Haulage) Ltd. in 1937 with four in line wheels on the steering fore-carriage and eight at the rear, all wheels on twin solids and on oscillating axles, was capable of carrying prodigious loads. Tom McTaggart, who drove for the firm at the relevant times, recorded a load on this trailer of a 110 ton boiler plus about 5 tons of timber packing.

In 1930, perhaps with his uncanny commercial acumen sensing how the coming slump was to affect the heavy haulage trade, Box approached Pickfords to see if they would take over his business. A price of £80 000 was agreed and on March 15 the transfer was completed. Box had ensured that a clause was written into the agreement appointing him manager of his erstwhile undertaking for five years. The mainline railways were empowered by the Railways (Road Transport) Act 1928 to own road transport undertakings, and they began the acquisition of road transport interests, commencing with buses. In 1933 they took a controlling interest in Hays Wharf Cartage Co. Ltd. which already owned Pickfords, so that Box's old firm indirectly came under the control of his old opponents. In 1941, Pickfords, wishing to expand their heavy haulage section, made a sufficiently enticing offer for Coulson & Co. Ltd. (Park Royal). In Scotland the LMS Railway acquired the business of Wordie & Co. Ltd., through whom they bought Road Engines & Kerr (Haulage) Ltd. For some time Robert Kerr, too, remained at the head of his old business.

These purchases by no means gave the railway companies a monopoly position as road heavy hauliers. Whether or not it had been the intention to seek other sellers in this field is not known. If such was the case it was never implemented, possibly because of the Second World War and its political aftermath. Probably the journey that secured most public notice during railway ownership was the epic run in January, 1938, from Cochrane's boiler works at Annan in Scotland to Beckton Gasworks, London, (a distance of 385 miles) hauling a steam accumulator 70 ft. long, 12 ft. in diameter, and weighing 90 tons. This took 21 days, and was undertaken by the former Box team after it had passed to Pickfords. The engines involved were all Fowlers, No.16263 *Talisman* and No.17105 *Atlas* hauling the accumulator, and No.16264 *Jix* hauling the living van and acting as banker.

Long distance heavy haulage by steam ended during the war except for the operations of Road Engines & Kerr. This came to an end in 1951, the business itself having been nationalised, along with Pickfords, in 1948. Local heavy haulage by steam hardly outlasted it. Dentons of Hyde, Cheshire, continued to make occasional use of their Fowlers Nos. 10318 (1905), and 14115 (1914) though their actual journeys and the date of the last are not well documented. Probably the last industrial users were John Thompson & Co. Ltd, the Wolverhampton boilermakers who kept steam going until 1971, using their Fowler B6 crane engine (No.17212 of 1929) and converted B6 showman's engine No. 19783 (1932) which originally worked for F.McConville as *King Carnival II,* but another late user was Thomas Bridson of Neston, Wirral, Cheshire. He was running his Fowler three speed road locomotive No.15276 (of 1920) until March, 1967, and would doubtless have found further work for it had he not died early in 1968.

The scales were tipped against the continuance of steam by a large number of small increments rather than by a single massive disadvantage.Manning was an important consideration. As Tom McTaggart has summed it up; in bad weather the driver kept fairly dry, the steersman was sometimes dry, depending on the direction of the wind, and the third man never dry. Crew comfort had showed marked improvement in most parts of the haulage industry after about 1930, but never reached traction engine crews. After the war with labour in a seller's market the poor conditions for the crew weighed against steam. Again, the days had passed when the time spent raising steam in the morning and clinkering off in the evening were accepted at no payment or nominal payment as part of the price of having a job at all. In the post-war period hours so spent had consequently to be paid for, and even then not everyone wanted to lose that amount of their leisure time. Consumable stores and spare parts for engines became harder to get and much dearer, and since road engines had ceased to be an article of commerce the question arose as to how long, in any event, those in use could be made to last. Speed too began to come into the calculation, not so much on the loaded run where the awkwardness of the load often fixed the rate of progress, but on the running light to the pick-up point and back to the depot after delivery. Finally there was the fact that the requisite alternative diesel engined plant was by then available. As it became a little more of a struggle to continue with steam there came the realisation that in this country it was no longer necessary to make the effort.

Had it been necessary to do so, one can gain some clues as to the likely course of events from the experience gained in East Germany where a sustained experiment was made in the post-war use of steam in heavy haulage. The origins were the culmination of an assessment of the possibilities of using solid fuel for road vehicles begun in the last days of the Nazi regime, and revived or recommenced on the establishment of the Democratic Republic. Two sizes of tractor were built, the smaller designed for an output of 70BHP at 800 r.p.m. and the larger for 120BHP at 1200 r.p.m. The load hauling capacities of the two types were stated to be 20 tons and 40 tons respectively at a service speed of 30 k.p.h. (about 19m.p.h.). The basis of each was a vertical water-tube boiler, hopper-fired with coke and pressed to 350 p.s.i. The engines were double acting, the smaller having two cylinders, and the larger three. In the latter the cylinders were 125mm diameter x 125mm stroke. The tractors carried some 340 gallons of water in two tanks, and were fully condensing. Barring accidents their water supplies could sustain, without top-up, the range of the fuel hoppers which was about 250 miles.

Their demise marked the end of serious efforts to use steam on the road for commercial purposes. As matters stand it is difficult to see what could lead to a revival of interest in steam, short of a total failure of oil supplies, or unsupportable atmospheric pollution from internal combustion exhausts. It was the latter that led to the Lear and other experimental steam buses in California in 1969-72. Three makers then produced vehicles for evaluation; Steam Power & Systems of San Diego; Lear Steam Motors Corporation of Reno, Nevada; and Brobeck of Berkeley. All were based upon liquid fired flash steam generators. The first-named used a six cylinder double acting compound engine, Lear used a turbine, and Brobeck used the Smith compound system with a 3½ inch diameter high pressure exhausting into two 4½ inch low pressure cylinders. All three contenders produced workable vehicles with clean exhaust but unless and until a cash value is placed upon the capacity to reduce atmospheric pollution there seems no prospect of any of them achieving a competitive cost in use compared with the mass-produced diesels with which they are in contention. There, so far as is known to the author, the matter rests.

Fig.85. *After Pickfords had taken over Norman Box's business* Talisman *(Fowler No.16263) traces* Atlas *(No.17105) on an unspecified but obviously very heavy load. Note, however, the immense improvements in the trailer compared with Fig.81.*

Fig.86. George Brotherwood's Foden No.726 in his yard at Medway Wharf, Tonbridge. On the left of the picture is the smokebox of Aveling & Porter 8NHP convertible No.3812 (1896).

Fig.87. Yorkshire No.1510 photographed by Derek Stoyel in August, 1934, at Poplar, newly painted in the colour of the then recently formed London Passenger Transport Board.

Fig.88. Alf Dawson's (Rushmere, Suffolk) Yorkshire No.1432 of 1917 found by Robert Pratt at Tattingstone, Suffolk, in June,1937, cluttered with the impedimentia of tarspraying.

Chapter 5

Old Soldiers

Foden outside framed wagon No.726 was delivered new to G.Brotherwood & Sons of Tonbridge, Kent, on March 19, 1904. When the firm ceased to trade in 1911 it went to E.P.Siggers & Co. in Tunbridge Wells and from them, in the following year, to Langley Motor Haulage Co. in Buckinghamshire and thence in 1919 to the Wenlock Brewery Co. Ltd. in London where, as their wagon no.1, it ran until 1934. A working life of thirty years for a vehicle produced in the infancy of wagon building was, in itself, worthy of note. In a curious way, too, it is linked into the story of the Road Locomotive Society. During its last year of life Derek Stoyel, then a young newcomer to the world of insurance in the City, was walking in the street with his friend Eric Preston whose interest in Foden wagons extended to noting the works number of each that he saw. The two young men and the old wagon met and Derek was despatched to the opposite pavement to make a note of the number. Most of those Eric had seen were in the twelve or thirteen thousands and when Derek reported that the number of this one was 726 they realised that they had encountered something rare. Derek's interest in road steam was founded that day and never waned thereafter. A little over three years later he became a founder member of the Society, in company with Eric Preston, who chaired the first meeting.

Venerable though the old Foden was of its class, its record for length of service was eclipsed by many rollers and ploughing engines and a by no means neglible number of traction engines. Its interest lies in the fact that its working lifetime encompassed virtually the whole period of commercial production of Foden wagons. Aside, however, from such early vehicles as No.726 there were other arresting steam wagons to be seen in London. Yorkshire, never a common make in the South of England, had at least three contenders for mention. One was the WG type (No.2181 of 1930) belonging to Gartons, the sugar refiners in Hammersmith, which was to be seen well into the post-war period. It always, in some fashion, gave the appearance of bustle and, indeed, was surprisingly nippy when circumstances permitted. The other two were Nos.1510 and 1511 (both new in 1925), a pair of 7-tonners fitted with gulley emptiers for cleansing the sumps of the London Passenger Transport Board's tramway conduits. Although the Board's policy had been to withdraw the steam wagons, mostly Fodens, which it had inherited with the London County Council tramways, it had not reached the two Yorkshires by the time war broke out in 1939 and, in consequence, they survived for another nine years. In terms of years they were not of great antiquity at the time they were scrapped. Most steam vehicles can carry a mere twenty-three years quite lightly, but the unorthodox layout of the Yorkshire and the fact of the two wagons being of a design already several years old when they were built left one after an encounter with No.1510 or its twin with the feeling of having seen something unusual and pleasurably archaic. Robert Pratt once remarked to the author of a somewhat similar feeling experienced after chancing across the late Alfred Dawson's Yorkshire (No.1432 of 1922) tar-spraying - battered, tar encrusted, and hung with buckets, chains, bags of coal, signs and tools.

The non-conformity of the Yorkshire's design to either the undertype or overtype arrangement was like an echo of the refusal of the Howard Brothers, forty years before, to build their traction and ploughing engines on conventional principles. Neither maker changed the views of the majority, but whereas the Yorkshire attained a reasonable level of sales the Howard brothers achieved no real acceptance of their engines. Alf Dawson's Yorkshire was not the only wagon to find a second career in tar spraying but in the trade's early days a number of new wagons were used under sprayers. Aitken's sprayers appeared on new Mann chassis, for instance, and Glossop's first sprayer of their patented design came out on Atkinson No.306 (1922), followed by several more on new chassis. In 1930 May Gurney & Co. of Norwich had Fodens Nos. 13708 and 13710 new, each fitted with a tar tank and sprayer whilst Robeys supplied new wagons to carry the burning and grouting machines designed by John Hines for the Allweather Mechanical Grouting Co.

By the late twenties, however, steam wagon sales were declining and after 1934, with the effects of the Salter Report, as we have already seen, new steam wagons, except for the Sentinel S range, were a spent commercial force. Good Fodens changed hands for £15 and such wagons, with ten or more years life expectancy were good raw material for tar-sprayers, which, as road making machines, paid only 5s.0d. a year tax. Glossops enlarged their fleet using Atkinsons and Sentinels, David Woods with Yorkshires and

Fig.89. In 1937 Alan Duke found Foden No.12208 in South Western Tar Distillers' depot by the A259 at Shoreham. It had come down in the world from the days when, owned by Fellingham & Co., the Brighton furniture removers, it had traversed the South and South-east with a lift van and trailer. Behind is a ship, stranded and filled around with solid material!

Fig.90. The last Yorkshire in commercial use in Britain was David Woods' No.2189 seen here in 1953. [G.R.Hawthorne]

Fig.91. Foden No. 13008 (1928) once a three-way tipper with Bethells of Sale, Ches., is, in the picture taken by Charles Lloyd on Good Friday, 1953, fitted up as a mobile mastic asphalt mixer (or cooker in the trade) with the Penmaenmawr & Trinidad Lake Asphalte Co.Ltd. The pulley and crossed belts on the cab roof drove the mixer paddles, to prevent uneven heating.

Fodens, and Norman Box mainly with Fodens, but some firms were omnivorous, using any cheap and sound chassis that came to hand. There can have been few makes that did not provide at least one chassis for a spraying outfit. Even some of the lethargic Clayton undertypes found a part they could fulfil in this way. Indeed No.UW2018 was actually exported new to Czechoslovakia in 1925 as a tar-sprayer. Tar spraying was an impecunious trade in which the competition for business was intense. Not only were there several major contenders for business on a national or semi-national scale but there were also a number of sizeable regional firms. Besides these some of the major gas companies, headed by the South Metropolitan Gas Co. of Greenwich, had entered the spraying market by contending successfully before the courts that a tanker/sprayer applying tar to the road surface was in fact 'delivering' its load, which was permissible within the legal powers under which they operated whereas the complete operation (spraying and gritting) of surface dressing was *ultra vires*. Engaging though this distinction was to the legal mind, no doubt, it left the rest of the surface dressing trade with a sense of grievance.

The following is a list in alphabetical order of some of the larger firms of tar spraying contractors. It is representative rather than comprehensive:

Aitken Taroads Syndicate Ltd.	Glasgow
Allweather Mechanical Grouting Co.Ltd.	London
Bituminous Road Products	Middlesborough
Box Grouting & Spraying Co.Ltd.	Altrincham
Bristowes Tarvia Ltd.	London
British Tarspraying Ltd.	Leeds
Burt, Boulton & Hayward Ltd.	London
Durable Roads Ltd.	London
W. & J.Glossop Ltd.	Hipperholme, Yorks.
Johnson Bros (Aylesford) Ltd.	Aylesford, Maidstone
Mechanical Tar Spraying & Grouting Co.Ltd.	London and Reading
National Road Dressing Co. Ltd.	Doncaster
Scientific Roads Ltd.	Shipley, Yorks.
Situsec Ltd.	London
H.V.Smith & Co. Ltd.	London
Taroads Ltd.	London
David Woods Ltd.	Yeadon, Yorks.

Besides all these and the gas companies there were also the direct labour forces of the various county councils ready to step in if the prices tendered for tarring showed a tendency to rise by even a few per cent. Consequently the rates for tarring secured by competitive tendering remained cut-throat. Thousands of miles in the late twenties and early thirties were swept, tarred, gritted, and rolled for rates of the order of 1½ old pence a square yard. In every aspect of the trade the participating firms had to enforce the most rigid economy and this applied not only to the steam wagons used to spray the tar, but also to the rollers employed to roll the grit.

If many old wagons found a respite from the scrapman by being converted to tar-sprayers so also a number of old and well worn steam rollers found a few extra years of life in chip-chasing. Perhaps the most remarkable metamorphosis was that of the Burrell 5-ton wagon No.3760 delivered new to Percy Wigg, the Lowestoft furniture remover, in 1917, which by 1923 had come into the hands of Edward J.Edwards, the Norwich road contractor. Finding it not over satisfactory as a wagon he took it apart in 1926, and used the engine and boiler as the basis of a three-point roller. Thus disguised it enjoyed another nine years of life.

Wear on the axle ends and in the wheel naves of a roller did not disqualify it from rolling in chippings. In fact a well-known roller owner and sometime surface dressing contractor once remarked that the freer the roller's wheels were to float on the axle the better they were able to follow the irregularities of road cambers and declivities. The peak of the surface dressing trade was probably about 1930. Most rural roads had been tar topped by that time and nearly all road authorities tried to tar-coat and grit them annually. With the use of improved tars and bitumen dressing materials, coupled with the enforced economies arising from the slump, authorities soon began to widen the intervals between top dressings, at first to two years, and then frequently in the war years and their aftermath, to three years.

Fig.92. Thomas Cowman & Sons Ltd. of Asfordby bought this ancient 10-ton Greens in the period of scarcity after 1918. It must have been useless for tar or bitumen bound material, but some use for road base or chip-chasing. Fred Gillford found it at Newstead Colliery, Leics., in May, 1925.

Fig.93. By contrast Greens No.2408, another 10-tonner but built in 1927 for Smith & Hutchinson of Leicester, shows a neat and well proportioned design.

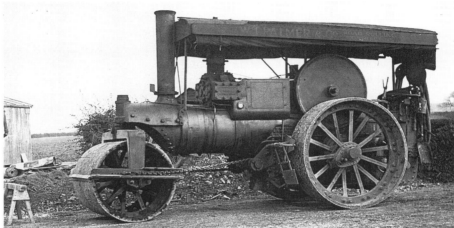

Fig.94. Aveling & Porter 15-tonner No.1565 (1880) lasted until the 1920's with Leicester Corporation, still with the conical front rolls as shown. [F.H.Gillford]

Fig.95. Like many contractors' rollers John Allen's No.44 began life in municipal ownership - in this case with Wolverhampton Corpn. The Aveling & Porter roller, No.7762, was built in 1912.

Most of the rollers employed were hired, a good many from the Eddison Steam Rolling Co. at Dorchester, by far the largest of the hiring firms and one, moreover, trading on a national scale, but also from the other large firms such as Bomford & Evershed of Salford Priors, Ford of Wokingham, Buncombe of Highbridge, Dingle of Kelly Bray (Cornwall), Allens of Oxford, Lancashire Road Rolling Co. of Altrincham, Arthur Cole of Sleaford, and Dickinsons of Emley who were prepared to follow a tarring gang wherever it went. Besides all these, hosts of purely local firms, urban and rural, picked up a share of the work. Lastly came the owner drivers, some of whom, like the late Alf Hope of Presteigne, were precise and careful in their habits and fastidious about the condition of the roller, others reckless to the point of idiocy. It is not proposed to name any of the latter variety but it is pleasant to dwell on the memory of Alf Hope and to recall sitting in the parlour of his little cottage while he discoursed on the knacks and hazards of working a roller on the steep slopes of the Welsh Border. "You can easily stop the wheels going round" he said in his melodious Border accent, recalling an incident when an engine had ended up broadside across a narrow road, "Doesn't mean to say you're going to stop the engine from sliding on the road."

In accidents by far the most vulnerable element of a roller was the front fork, closely followed by the forecarriage head. A runaway brought to a sudden stop against a kerb or bank or even another vehicle often ended up on its knees through the breakage of the fork or forecarriage head. The late Harry Pitts of Aveling & Porter was once asked by a leading roller owner why his firm did not use cast steel for these items. "Because then you wouldn't break enough" came the reply, perhaps demonstrating that the spare parts trade did not become a lucrative business only with the arrival of the motor car.

Notwithstanding these hazards, rollers had very long working lives. Wallis & Steevens No.2149 of 1890, the first of its genre sold in this country, survived to the very end of steam rolling and is in preservation today. Built for Carter Bros. of Billingshurst, it worked for them for fifty-one years and spent several more in service with Andrew Harvey of Partridge Green, a few miles away. Perhaps even more remarkable was the survival of one of the Aveling Batho type rollers at the Elan Valley Reservoir in Wales for maintaining the roads there. It was seen by visiting Society members and photographed by several in 1937, but unfortunately its owners seem not to have appreciated what an historic machine they possessed and soon afterwards it was cut up for scrap. Equally astonishing was the long life of Aveling & Porter No.1241 of 1876 built to the design which superseded the Batho type, with conical front rolls mounted on down pointed stub axles on either side of a central spindle or column. Because of the coning of the front wheels and the slight inclination of the axles upon which they were mounted they ran edge to edge at the road surface but sufficiently far apart at the top to allow the vertical spindle to pass between them. Here again the roller existed in the service of the Port of Spain Municipality in Trinidad until 1953 when it was cut up, so far as one can judge, without a second thought as to its historical significance.

Curious though this arrangement of the front rolls was, engines equipped with it remained in use for many years. Jesse Ellis of Maidstone had two examples in service up to the time his firm was wound up in 1907; Thomas Turner of Chelsea had another, and there were sundry others in the provinces. The late Fred Gillford recalled one in Leicester c.1925 and commented that the differential speeds at the meeting edges and outer ends of the front rolls respectively produced a peculiar scuffing action which seemed not to have been unduly troublesome on water bound road materials but something of a disaster when rolling chippings or tarmacadam. The combination of road improvements to meet the demands of cycle and motor traffic and the spread of tar or bitumen bound surfaces and asphalt roads produced an increasing demand for the services of steam rollers during the first quarter of this century, which ensured that few rollers were scrapped in that period, though some of the rollers which were sent to the Western Front and other theatres of war between 1914 and 1918 were either lost by enemy action or not repatriated. On the whole there had been few losses by the time the slump and the consequent hire rate cutting hit the rolling trade about 1932. From then on old rollers were scrapped at an increasing rate.

Though production of new steam rollers came down to a trickle at that time the demands for the competing petrol or oil engined rollers also all but stagnated. Mostly hirers were concerned solely with simply holding on, keeping their old plant going and hoping for better times. They were better able to keep steam alive because they did not have the problem of short term intermittent use that municipal users experienced. A hirer's roller was either on hire or not. Its use might have been intermittent in the sense that a few weeks of work might alternate with an equal period when it remained unhired but even so it faced a different problem to that of the municipal roller. Indeed the justification advanced for the

Fig. 96. *On its knees in Watford High Street, c.1910, near the subsequent site of Woolworths is an unidentified Aveling & Porter roller, its forks smashed in a collision with a heavy horse-drawn dray.*

Fig. 97. *R.E.Palmer of Great Massingham, Norfolk, was a roller owner, engine dealer, repairer and, from time to time and very reluctantly, a scrapman. Because he was so hesitant about breaking up engines many that passed through his hands survived to be preserved. This is his 10-ton Wallis & Steevens No.7757 (1922).*

Fig. 98. *Eddison Steam Rolling Co's No.6, an Aveling & Porter (No.2833) built in 1891. Eddison would go anywhere and roll anything.*

municipal ownership of a roller was often that of availability at short notice. A council's roller might do no more than two or three hours of actual work a day but it was expected to be available whenever wanted. In practice, with a steam roller, this often meant being in steam six days a week yet doing no more than fifteen or twenty hours of actual rolling. An internal combustion roller, assuming that it was in reasonable condition, could be started up on demand, cutting down the wasted hours. The appeal of the petrol or diesel roller to a borough engineer often hinged on this.

Plenty of hirers would, no doubt, have been glad to have been free of the burden of annual boiler inspections, boiler insurance, washing out of boilers, and retubing, but the price to be paid for this freedom would have been a capital outlay upon which there was no hope of a return. Many owners did not have such money of their own, and, even had they been willing to burden themselves with bank or finance house borrowing to provide the capital, not all of them would have been deemed to have had good enough collateral to secure the loan.

Bomford & Evershed who found their workshop facilities underused because of the effect of the recession upon other parts of their business decided upon a compromise. Eric Alley, grandson of Stephen Alley, founder of the Sentinel Waggon Works, was at that time on the technical staff at Salford Priors. He was told to prepare drawings for the conversion of part of their fleet of steam rollers to diesel propulsion by cutting off the original engine of the roller together with part of the top of the boiler, forming a new flat top to the boiler and mounting thereon a three cylinder Fowler B type diesel engine of 40HP connected through forward and reverse clutches to the original gear train of the roller. The cost was, of course, very much less than that of a new diesel roller but despite the engineering expertise that Eric Alley was able to deploy onto the task the result remained an uncomfortable hybrid. The engine position was the only practicable one in the circumstances, but the resulting layout was about as far as could be imagined from what the designer would have selected had he been starting from first principles. John Allen & Sons also converted some of their single cylinder Avelings (and, it is believed, some for outside customers) by mounting a Marshall single cylinder double flywheel two stroke oil engine on top of the boiler, using the boiler and firebox water spaces as a cooling water reservoir from which the water was circulated by a belt-driven pump. The main bulk fuel storage was in the old water tank from which oil was lifted as required by a hand-operated semi-rotary pump to a gravity feed tank under the roof.

Hand-starting oil engines of this type was a hazard and would have been a rotten job even with the feet on the ground. Being perched high up on a footboard made it worse. Allens put twin footboards to enable two starting handles to be used but it was not a task to be envied. Bomfords and Allens persevered with the use of their conversions but the rest of the trade looked at them, shrugged (at least figuratively) and went on using what they had. Within their limitations the conversions were quite workable and some had relatively long lives in their new form. In 1965 the author came across one in a contractor's site compound in New Ross in the Irish republic. At Eddison Victor Garrett and his chief engineer, Charles Stewart, pondered the results of conversions and decided to stay with steam until circumstances permitted its replacement by purpose built diesel rollers. Had the requisite funds been available they would have re-equipped with Aveling Barford DX and DY type diesels, but the money was not there, and consequently their steamers soldiered on.

A few diehards with the necessary funds bought new steam rollers in the thirties. J.H.Fisher of Burghfield, near Reading, had Wallis & Steevens Advance No.8085 new in May, 1933, a bold act of faith when the trade and its prospects seemed to have reached their nadir, and when the future seemed to be with internal combustion. His was the last Wallis & Steevens steamer sold to a hirer in the mainland of Britain though No.8088 went fourteen months later to Mitchell, Nutt & Colgan at Claudy, Co.Derry. Another firm that astonished its contemporaries in the trade was Banes & Co. of Potton, Bedfordshire. Beginning modestly with two old Aveling & Porter 10-ton singles (No.3319 of 1893 and No.5878 of 1905) Banes went on to purchase, between 1931 and 1943, a fleet of eight new rollers beginning with Aveling & Porter 10-ton slide valve singles but concluding with two Aveling Barford AC type 8-tonners and a pair of AE type 10-tonners sold by Aveling Barford after the move to Grantham. In the late thirties Banes & Co. took work at prices that left the opposition gasping. The trade believed, probably rightly, that Banes was subsidised in this expenditure by Edward Barford who subsequently became the owner of the firm and used it as a vehicle for acquiring (in 1946) the business of the Eddison Steam Rolling Co. The present Eddison firm is in fact the Banes company with its name changed.

Fig.99. Aveling & Porter three-shaft convertible (No. 986 of 1874) owned by Wm. Lambert, father of the famous Chris. They finally broke up the old engine in 1915.

Fig.100. The four-shaft version of an A & P convertible. This is No.2527 (1889) owned by T. T. Boughton of Amersham Common, when it was much more rural than now.

Fig.101. The unidentified Aveling Batho type roller was found at the Elan Valley reservoir in Wales during an RLS visit in 1937 where it had been used to maintain the private roads. Like many such historic machines it was subsequently broken up.

The outbreak of war with its resultant demand for rollers, coupled with the difficulty of obtaining diesel-engined replacements then or in the immediate post-war years, kept a substantial number of rollers in service until the early nineteen-fifties, but thereafter erosion of numbers was fairly rapid though still not total. By 1970 the number of steam rollers in commercial use was down to a handful. This stay of execution led to some unexpected survivals. Aveling & Porter single No.1760 (1882) was used for many years by Reading Corporation. When they had no further use for it at the end of the thirties they offered it for sale with the proviso that the purchaser should break it up for scrap. Why this officious clause should have been inserted can only be guessed at. Perhaps it merely illustrates the devious thinking of the true bureaucrat. Whatever the intention may have been, it was frustrated. The successful bidder was Arthur Ford of Wokingham. Finding the roller to be in excellent condition he quietly shipped it off, as No.13 in his fleet, to a distant part of the county and set it to work. On the death of Arthur Ford in 1942, John Allen & Sons (Oxford) Ltd. bought a 50% share in his business of Ford (Wokingham) Ltd. In 1951 the company was reconstructed as John Allen & Ford Ltd, taking over the John Allen fleet of rollers in addition to its own. No.1760 survived all these changes and in 1959 worked on the construction of the M1 motorway. The next year it was repurchased by Aveling Barford Ltd. for preservation.

A retired soldier who became a figure of exceptional interest in steam dredging was Colonel Edward Mornement of East Harling, Norfolk, where he became a ploughing and threshing contractor in the eighteen-nineties, using three sets of Fowler 14NHP singles (1763 and 1764 of 1872; 2391 and 2392 of 1872; and 2900 and 2901 of 1878) together with a slightly newer pair of 10NHP Burrells (894 and 895 of 1882/83) and various Burrell and McLaren traction engines. He was also involved in the firm of Mornement & Wright Ltd, which had taken over what remained of the business of the South Western Counties Steam Cultivating Company. The Mornement & Wright business was based at Alton, Hants, though the registered office was at East Harling. The Colonel later withdrew from this business in favour of E.W. & E.H.Wright, but continued at East Harling in partnership with J.M.C.Ray as Mornement & Ray Ltd.

The parlous times through which steam ploughing and cultivating had passed doubtless encouraged both of Colonel Mornement's firms, as earlier it had Bomford & Evershed, to take up dredging, but the works for which he most deserves to be remembered, and which came perilously close to being forgotten altogether, had it not been for the researches of Frank Strange, were those of dredging the Fen drains and constructing the sea bank at Wingland, in the Wash. The Fen country of South Lincolnshire and Cambridgeshire had been drained and brought into cultivation mainly in the eighteenth century, under the direction of Dutch engineers, but by a hundred years later the channels had become silted to an extent that produced a serious loss of water capacity. Colonel Mornement's firms had done a limited amount of double engine scoop dredging and had also done dredging from pontoons using grabs mounted on steam cranes and discharging either into barges or onto the bank in restricted waterways.

The dredging of the Fen drains presented problems seldom encountered elsewhere. The drains were, relatively at least, narrow, with steeply graded banks, while the working space available at the top of the bank was often severely restricted in width and of low bearing capacity. Moreover as noted earlier, the bridges which had to be traversed were notoriously restrictive, being frequently of wood and maintained to a standard which could be described as no better than indifferent. These conditions militated against the use of ploughing engines for dredging since their bulk and weight would have been a handicap whilst their capacity for long pulls, so useful when dredging a lake, could not have been used to the full. Instead the firm designed a new pattern of scoop and developed a system that made use of traction engines. As the contracts were for a public body (the Fen Commissioners) they were presumably secured by public tender, but whether the firm first designed its equipment and then, on the strength of it, made a successful tender for the first contract or whether, on the other hand, they made their bid and only then worked out how to do the work is a question to which the answer is unlikely to be known. The truth is probably that Colonel Mornement may well have had the germ of the idea in his head before bidding but worked it out in detail only when the first tender was accepted.

What he did was to place a substantial steel sling strap round the boiler immediately in front of the throat plate. This carried either end of the vertical spindle of the roping sheave. To maintain the sheave in its working position a stay rod ran forward from its bracket to an anchor point on the smokebox. Both sling and stay had turn buckles for adjustment. The rope ran off the drum, through the sheaves and then off at, or near, right angles to the engine's rear side, the rope thimble being anchored to the scoop. The engines worked in pairs, usually an 8NHP, preferably a compound, on the pulling-in side, and a smaller engine, probably a 6NHP, on the other bank pulling-out. The operation was conducted by the smaller engine drawing out the rope against the larger engine's resistance, the rope kept taut by a judicious use of the reverser, until the scoop was over the starting position of the pull when it would be dropped in from the greatest height possible so as to cut into the weed and silt. The puller-in would then haul out the scoop and contents to the top of the bank. In favourable conditions there was enough space to discharge the scoop clear of the engine, but in congested spots it often had to be emptied round the engine itself which thus stood knee-deep in black mud. A bystander was once heard to make a remark euphemistically reported to have been to the effect that he could not understand how men could work year in, year out, in mud up to their earholes. The mud never actually got that high and the reader is left to conjecture what the original remark might have been. The working was one way and the completion had to be done from the other bank, either by the first pair swapping sides if a bridge was conveniently near or by a second pair of engines. In many cases bridges had to be crossed with circumspection, using spreader timbers on the decks and sometimes shoring timbers underneath as well. Accidents involving Fen bridges collapsing under the weight of an engine are on record but not, so far as is known, ever under that of a Mornement & Ray dredging engine.

Though Mornement & Ray had a depot in Boston overhauls and major repairs were done in East Harling. The work was hard on differential bevels despite the use of phophor bronze replacements. Running repairs were done on site by the crews, only major troubles meriting a visit from an East Harling fitter. A complete gang, to work four engines and two scoops, was made up of six men and a foreman, sometimes with a cook boy or trainee in addition. With the jobs being situated in such distant and lonely places the gangs normally lived in vans. Fat salt bacon was a staple food, usually with bread or potatoes, sometimes with eggs. Cheese, jam, tinned milk, tea and sugar were other standbys. Water was a problem, and for both drinking and boiler feed, it often had to be carted to the sites along the banks, though if at all possible, water from the drain was used for the boilers.

In the period from 1900 to the first war the engine strength was mainly Burrells, but in the aftermath of the war the firm bought six 10NHP McLaren compounds, Nos.1613, 1621, 1622, 1624, 1625, and 1626, originally delivered in 1918 to the War Department. Though nearly new engines when bought they were soon put to gruelling use. For some years the Crown Commissioners had been engaged on the embanking of a large area of salt marsh at Wingland with a view to detaching it from the sea so that it could be drained and brought into cultivation. Begun before the war with local hand labour and continued during the war by German prisoners it was incomplete and in the doldrums by the time Mornement & Ray secured the contract to complete it in the twenties. In order to carry out the work two engines were positioned on rafts in the tideway to pull back the scoops. Twice each day the unfortunate engines were immersed by the rising tide whilst still in steam, a very destructive process even by the standards of the Fen dredging trade. Whereas dredging the drains had involved damming off the length to be dredged, and consequently could only be undertaken when this could be done without danger of the back-up water causing flooding, i.e. broadly in the summer and autumn, at Wingland the work went on all the year round, subject only to the length of days and the state of the terrain. The work was hard, rough, and dirty, but still welcome to the men engaged in it as it provided work through the depressed days of the late twenties in South Lincolnshire. Mornement & Ray seem to have enjoyed a better relationship with their employees than many firms at that time, and men worked for them continuously for years at a stretch. Wingland came to an end about 1931 but other Fenland contracts continued and most of the men went on in Mornement & Ray's employ. Indeed, for many, service with the firm came to an end only with the second war and the death of Colonel Mornement, Mr. Ray having gone from the scene many years before.

Despite the roughness of the job the engines were regularly overhauled and kept in as good a condition as the circumstances would allow. Certainly the company were not heedless or neglectful owners but nor, on the other hand, were they likely to have harboured sentimental feelings towards their engines. Though we now may shudder at the effects of standing the McLarens in the sea at Wingland, it must be remembered that, economically speaking, they were simply expendable items of plant, bought cheaply, and small in value in relation to the overall sums involved in the contract. Nevertheless, where possible, efforts were made to minimise the effect on the engines of an exceptionally onerous job. Water was piped to each engine so that the use of salty or brackish water was avoided. Despite the apparent crudity of the

Fig.102. Few pictures were taken of the Mornement & Ray McLarens on the Wingland project but one is shown here on the timber support raft upon which it stood during work.

methods employed nothing, in fact, was improvised. Everything used was designed to be simple and exceptionally rugged.

After the Colonel was gone the dredging work slipped away. Three of the McLarens migrated to Somerset to work with a similar engine on the dredging of the Huntspill watercourse in Somerset as part of the arrangements for a war-time munitions factory. The remainder passed to Watson Bros. of Whittlesey, also dredging contractors, by whom they were briefly and desultorily used, finally going for scrap with the exception of No.16, *Boadicea,* which survives, rebuilt to its original form and condition, whilst in the hands of Anthony Heal.

Perhaps they were the ultimate in old soldiers, built for a war which was over almost as they were completed; used between the wars in what must be considered the nearest peacetime equivalent to front line service, and, as almost their last gesture, used on war-work in the second world war.

Fig.103. One of the pair of Ottomeyer-built double cylinder ploughing engines preserved at the Moor Museum, Gross Hesepe, Emsland, Germany.

103

Fig.104. A nearly forgotten aspect of the home grown timber trade. E.J.Barnes & Sons' 1905 8NHP Burrell (No.2779) Walter Long, near Swindon in 1913 with oak bark for the use of tanners.

Fig.105. An unknown Allchin 7NHP single at work in the yard of Benjamin Horton at Westerham.[W.Newell]

Fig.106. W.E.Chivers & Sons were builders, sawmillers and haulage contractors in Devizes. Here their 7NHP three speed sprung road engine, Burrell No.3633 of 1914, Lord Kitchener, is halted in Winchester. It is preserved by Bobbie King at Headcorn, Kent

Chapter 6

Timber to the Mill

When William Henry Giles (b.1877) died at Gayton, on the outskirts of Kings Lynn, in November, 1959, a trade practised in this country since remote antiquity died with him, for Bill was a lath render, a craftsman in rending or riving of wooden laths for plasterers, cleft along the grain of the wood, without sawing, infinitely stronger and more resilient than sawn laths which, for a few years, were used in their place. Though thought by many to have been a Norfolk man Bill was, in fact, born in Far Cotton near Northampton where he had learned his trade before moving, at the age of twenty, to work for T.Stanton & Co. in Kings Lynn, the firm with whom he remained for the rest of his working life.

A great many other aspects of the home grown timber trade besides lath rending have changed dramatically in the last fifty years. Some, such as the cleaving out of oak boarding for fences, have dwindled to extinction whilst others, such as the making of besom brooms, the cleaving of oak or chestnut shingles, and the burning of charcoal, are shadows of what they once were. Making faggots from the tops and trimmings of coppice grown wood is abandoned. Whereas faggots were once used for the bases of stacks, for fuelling brick ovens, and for firing brick kilns, all the tops now go onto the bonfire. On the other hand, by way of a partial balance, there is a market for smaller diameter hardwood for pulp making that never existed fifty or sixty years ago.

In the early years of this century, most country estates had a permanent sawmill or wood lodge in which timber felled on the estate was converted into material for gates, fences and buildings. Though a number were powered by a horse-work or by a water wheel, the majority were driven by a portable engine, a locomobile, or a fixed engine. The Redleaf estate sawmill belonging to the Hills family at Camp Hill, Chiddingstone Causeway, Kent, was driven by a 10NHP double cylindered Wallis & Steevens portable (No.2010 of 1884). That on the adjoining Hall Place estate of Lord Hollanden was powered by a Ransomes portable. On the other hand, the sawmill on the Duke of Northumberland's estate at Albury, near Guildford, was driven by a Fowler two speed spring mounted traction engine (No.15466) which, fortunately, survives into preservation. Village wheelwrights and farmers on the whole did not have fixed sawmills but relied upon the saw-pit or the travelling rack-bench. The saw-pit at 'Potty' Faircloth's wheelwright's shop in Leigh, Kent, the author's home village, existed and remained in occasional use well into the thirties. In the prime of the trade a wheelwright would buy his trees standing, then had them felled, and carted them home. Subsequently they were converted and the timber was seasoned on his own premises. When the saw-pit was used, sawing was done, mostly by contract, by gangs of travelling sawyers noted for their drunkeness and for riotous behaviour generally, this probably forming the only available antidote for the dreadful monotony of their trade. Latterly it was the custom to have the conversion done by power, most often by steam, and again often by contract. Here the travelling rack saw-bench taken round by a traction engine came into its own, though portables were also used. Farmers, too, were customers of the portable rack-bench though a farmer's needs - gate posts, fencing material and squared timber for farm buildings - could be satisfied with raw material much inferior to that required by a wheelwright, particularly if the latter worked in the carriage trade. Hence work on a farm often consisted of running out fence or gate posts from the major limbs of big oaks, the prime butts of which had been sold to a local sawmiller or builder.

At Oxted, in south-east Surrey, the Williams family, who were village builders - at a time when a good class village builder could do country house work or church work to the highest standards, including stone masonry and elaborate joinery - had an 8NHP Fowler for this purpose and for the general haulage work of the business. A country firm of similar antecedents was Chivers & Sons of Devizes where the transport side of the business eventually developed to the point of the tail wagging the dog.

Hauling timber by steam had a long pedigree. Timber was one of the loads the Boydell engine hauled on its celebrated and often reported trip from Thetford to Woolwich in 1857, probably the earliest directly recorded instance, though circumstantially one can deduce that steam was used for carting round timber from the time the traction engine first became capable of the task. It was one of the duties performed by George Ellis of Brenchley, Kent, with his old Aveling No.690 (1871) which was also used to power the rack-bench and for threshing. Other instances could be cited from various parts of the country during the

Fig.107. The high wheeled Aveling & Porter in use by the Jarvises of Bethersden, Kent, c.1905, to power the portable rack bench is not identified, but the shape of the wording on the name plate is not inconsistent with its being owned by Jesse Ellis & Co. Ltd. of Maidstone. Arthur Jarvis (1878-1969) is in the right foreground and Ernest Hukins, the driver, stands in front of the smokebox.

Fig.108. A gear drive Tasker B2 (No.1399), owned by Francis Grover, hauling timber into the railway goods yard at Uxbridge, Middlesex.

seventies and eighties. Nevertheless the weight and bulk of a traction engine of 6NHP and upwards was a limitation on its sphere of usefulness in off-the-road work and, indeed, even on the roads themselves. As we have already seen bridges having onerous weight restrictions were a particular obstacle, whilst the doctrine of extraordinary traffic was almost as considerable an impediment.

The beech woods of the Chiltern Hills, the source of timber for the chair makers of the High Wycombe district, supported a group of timber hauliers and timber merchants who became well-known. Jonathan Plumridge & Sons were timber merchants and sawmillers in High Wycombe itself. Their 6NHP Fowler compound B3 road loco *Progress* became a familiar sight in the district, but probably the firm which became best known in the years before the 1914 war was that founded by Thomas Trafford Boughton at Chenies Manor, Buckinghamshire, and transferred to Bell Lane, Amersham, in 1909. T.T.Boughton & Sons became known for many things beside timber haulage. They undertook threshing, had a fleet of steam rollers, and were repairers of engines and tackle. In more recent years they designed, patented, and constructed a winch for timber tractors, founded upon their own experience in timber haulage. Thomas Boughton had three 8NHP Aveling & Porter engines all bought second-hand from the Road Breaking Company in London. The oldest was *Ethel,* No.4353 of 1899, the next in line was *Croydon,* No.4521 of 1900, and the newest was *Moonlight,* No.4755 of 1901. The two earlier engines were singles, but *Moonlight* was compound and spring-mounted into the bargain which made it the favourite for the longer timber hauls. Though more comfortable to ride on than the singles it was not noted for speed and its name was said to come for its propensity for arriving home after the moon had risen.

At one time *Ethel* had the distinction of being driven and steered by two Franks, Frank Grover as driver and Frank Honour as steersman, both later to be timber hauliers in their own right. After what turned out to be a false start as a general haulier (1913-16) using steam wagons, Frank Grover received the chance of a new start in the more specialised business of hauling round timber when in 1919 he was offered a twelve month contract by Francis Groves, who was a timber merchant in nearby Chesham and formerly a customer of Boughtons. Not wishing to be underhand Francis Grover went to his erstwhile employer and asked him directly if he had any objection to him (Francis Grover) setting up in competition so near at hand. The older man replied that there was room for both of them and wished him luck. As a result of this openness on the one hand and broad-mindedness on the other, the two remained on good terms as long as Thomas Boughton lived. February 5, 1919, was a momentous day for Frank Grover. On it he became the owner of Tasker B2 tractor No. 1899 for £400.0.0, lent to him by his father. The engine came from a sale of plant at Joseph Arnold's sand quarry at Leighton Buzzard, together with a trailer wagon. Soon afterwards, finding work plentiful, he bought another B2, No.1407, from Gooderal Brothers, High Wycombe, generally similar to the first but carrying 180lb. pressure, where the slightly older engine had only 160lb. In the post-war period of engine shortage this cost him £550.0.0.

By October the post-war boom in engines was in decline. In that year Francis was able to buy from Birch Sawmills in High Wycombe, a further Tasker B2 (three speeder No.1746 of 1917) together with two Tasker built timber tugs for only £450.0.0 with a discount of £25.0.0. for clearing the debt within six months. Thus when still under thirty he had three sets of tackle at work hauling in timber not only from his native Buckinghamshire, but also from the neighbouring counties of Berkshire, Oxfordshire, Hertfordshire and Middlesex, to the many sawmills then at work in the Berkhamsted, Chesham and High Wycombe areas. Because the three speeder was such a willing engine Frank admitted to flogging it along - timber haulage was, after all, on a piece-work rate and a low one at that - so that it developed broken spokes in the rear wheels. By 1925 the state of affairs was so bad that he ordered from Taskers a pair of replacement wheels with pressed-on rubbers, for which he paid £194.0.0., nearly half what he had paid for the engine. They transformed the situation, eliminating broken spokes, and improving the riding qualities. In turn, the improved riding caused the third speed - the furthest from the overhung bearing - to be used more. The crankshaft broke twice on the gear side of the bearing. The third time it happened Frank did not replace it but sold the engine to Boughtons.

Whilst this was going on, Frank had become interested in the chain driven version of the B2. Eventually he owned three of them and his story of how he came to do so is so interesting and full of the atmosphere of steam in the twenties that it is quoted verbatim:

"It would be about the end of 1923 when Harry Shepherd, an engine dealer of Luton, was trying to sell a Foden wagon to the Dorking Brick Company, who would only do business if he took in part-payment their Tasker tractor. Harry knew Mr.Boughton and tried to get him interested in this engine, but the price asked, £150, was too much. Mr.Boughton

Fig.109. The 8NHP Clayton & Shuttleworth compound road loco (No.45125), which was driven by 'Pincher' (who slept in a tarpaulin under the engine) and operated by Charles Miles & Sons of Stamford, Lincs.

Fig.110. Tom Newell's Garrett tractor No. 33078 was getting out a loaded tug downhill to the road for haulage by one of his Aveling tractors. A log dragged on a chain helped the braking but the chain broke and the load ran away, pushing the engine over. Jack Newell was driving and went out through the roof, not long before the picture was taken. [W.Newell]

Fig.111. When his brother Bill returned with the Aveling they pulled the engine upright, improvised a repair to the chimney and went back to work with it. The near side rear wheel was slightly buckled, and it was never used for road work again, nor was the roof put back. [W.Newell]

therefore got in touch with me and we came to an agreement whereby he bought my first tractor, No.1399, for £50, and I bought the Dorking Brick Co's engine for £150. Having made arrangements, we went to Dorking to collect this engine, which was another Class B2 three-speed 'Little Giant' tractor, No.1760, built for the War Department and fitted with chain drive. The front tank was longer than standard and therefore of greater capacity, and the registration number was FA695. Certain items of equipment were known to be missing, and Reg Ratcliffe and I therefore had to take with us on the train to Dorking a lift pipe, clinker shovel, and poker. It was quite a long way from the station to the brickworks, which was actually at Holmwood, but eventually we reached the engine and steamed it for the journey home.

The difference between the riding of this chain drive and the previous gear driven engines was unbelievable. It rode like a steam wagon and nearly as fast. I resolved to buy no more gear drive tractors after this and keep my eyes open only for chain drives. The chain drive was also considerably quieter and this was noticed particularly by my wife, who could hear a gear drive engine, especially if it was No.1746, coming a long time before we reached home. On the other hand, I could get the chain drive home without her hearing it at all, so that she would be surprised to see me come indoors.

Having done a considerable amount of business with Taskers and been to the Waterloo Iron Works on many occasions, they knew I was enthusiastic about their chain drive tractors. Thus in 1925, when they had an order for a 6-ton three-speed wagon from Bradford & Sons Ltd. of Poole, and had to take in part-payment a chain drive tractor, No.1670, they thought of me. This engine had been supplied new to Bradfords at their Yeovil depot in 1915, had the registration No. AA5679, and was named *Shamrock*. Mr.Hoare and Mr.Gibbs of the firm came up from Andover to call on me at Amersham, and when they eventually found me I was asked if I would buy No.1670. I agreed at once and said I would have the engine straight away, Taskers lending Bradfords a two-speed gear drive tractor, No.1409, during the time their new wagon was being built. Bradford's driver was at once horrified with the uncomfortable riding of the gear drive and demanded to have *Shamrock* back. The situation was explained to me and, knowing how he felt, I agreed to lend it to them, provided Taskers put right any defects which had occurred in the meantime.

In due course I received *Shamrock* back, the firm being as good as their word, and the engine was in fine condition, in a new coat of paint with my name on the canopy sides. Because it looked so smart when delivered under its own steam my neighbours thought that I had just bought a new engine. *Shamrock* had driving wheels 10in. wide, of single tee-ring section, and after a time I fitted these with rubber cross strakes supplied by a firm called Millers from somewhere up North. These strakes were cut from solid rubber tyres and would have proved very successful if they had all been of the same thickness, which they were not. The result was that, although the engine ran with less vibration than on steel shoes, the riding was somewhat bumpy, and could not really be considered as satisfactory. With the coming of this second chain drive tractor the earlier gear drive engine, No.1407, became surplus to requirements and Boughtons kept coming round to borrow parts to keep one of their own engines going. They intended to replace these parts but never seemed to do so, and eventually it was arranged that they should buy the whole engine and take it away.

In 1927 Taskers had got into financial trouble and went into liquidation, one of the results being the putting up for sale of a number of engines, including No.1741, a Class B2 chain drive tractor which had been supplied new to Albert Aylett of East Dean in 1917, and subsequently returned to the makers. The registration number of this engine was HO2040, and I bought it for £130, the firm agreeing to do it up, including repainting, lining out, and putting my name on the canopy sides. They delivered No.1741 by road under its own steam and it looked so smart that my friends and neighbours thought I had yet another brand new engine. It was somewhere about this time that my brother left me to go and drive a new Super Sentinel tractor No.6816 that had been delivered to Jesse Wright of Chesham."

Tractors were all very well up to a point, if part of a small and closely watched set-up owned by a man such as Francis Grover, a capable mechanic and thoroughly knowledgeable driver. Where they did not do so well was in firms where they were mere ancillaries to the main business and where the owners either knew little of how they ought to have been managed and driven or, alternatively, were too preoccupied with other, wider, aspects of the business to give them much attention. Timber hauling was a rough trade, hard on the men who worked in it and, even in the stricken condition of employment in the slump years, one in which only a limited number of men were prepared to work. It is not altogether surprising, therefore, that drivers were no more tender towards the plant than the job itself was to them. This is not to say there were no drivers who cossetted the engine but they were not numerous. Timber hauliers' drivers could, and often did, display great sagacity in snigging out trees from awkward spots, loading in difficult situations, and extricating the loaded timber tug from sticky terrain, but in the process the engine was liable to get the same treatment as the horses - well thrashed.

For this reason traction engines continued to be used for timber haulage well into the twenties by such firms as Boughtons; Charles Miles of Stamford, Lincolnshire; the Stowmarket Timber Co. in Suffolk; and Wears of Hexham, Northumberland. Others were torn between, on the one hand, the desire for something lighter and faster, and on the other, the self-evident trouble other people had with tractors in the hands of paid drivers. As with all such questions there were secondary considerations. A traction with its much larger winding drum could carry a 50 yard rope of ⅝ in. diameter whereas almost without exception tractors had only ½ in. ropes and no more than 30 yards on the drum. The Garrett No.4 tractor, having a big drum, could carry 50 yards of ⅝ in. rope. In case an extra eighth of an inch in diameter is felt to be a small thing it is perhaps timely to recall that since cross-sectional area and hence tensile strength, goes as the square of the diameter, the strength of a ⅝ in. rope compared with that of a ½in. is in the ratio of 25:16. The bigger ropes and drums, however, added to the labour of pulling the rope out. It was a lucky day if a horse was available to do it, - usually it fell to the lot of the loader. Again, a traction

Fig.112. Wallis & Steevens 7-ton tractor No.7966, owned by Paul Wadey, of Dorking, roping out its loaded tug onto a narrow road.

Fig.113. No.7966 coupled up to two tugs ready to move off. Both tugs are still on steel tyres.

Fig.114. The "fierce and powerful engine" in person - Foden No.12670, originally Billy Smith's King of the Forest, *sold to Francis Grover and finally, in 1935, passing to T.T.Boughton & Sons.*

engine legally needed two men to manage it and the police were vigilant to see this rule was not transgressed. A tractor needed only one.

The raising of the permissible weight of conventional tractors did very little for the dilemma. Wallis & Steevens, for instance, produced a 7 ton tractor in the mid-twenties but sales were a grievous disappointment. No.7966, built in the early twenties, hung about the works unsold, though often demonstrated, until it eventually was sold in 1930, at a knocked-down price, to Paul Wadey of Dorking, Surrey, who had it for hauling round timber but found it a tame performer beside its competitors which, by that time, included Foden and Sentinel steam tractors, and the Latil petrol engined tractor. Had timber hauling remained exclusively a preserve of the steam engine the Foden and Sentinel tractors would have transformed it. In the second half of the twenties they did indeed make a big impression on those in the trade who were in a position to buy new engines. This included some of the sawmill owners and a few of the major firms of hauliers, but most hauliers were one man businesses where the operating margins were too narrow to afford new engines.

The Foden 'D' type tractor, purpose built for the job and carrying 230 psi. boiler pressure had a punch and snap in it not found in such a thing as an old Wallis & Steevens oil-bath tractor working at 160 psi. Frank Grover once described the D-type as a "fierce and powerful engine", as indeed it was. It was, moreover, equipped with a powerful winch mounted under the rear of the tractor but, again, with a snag. Putting it into or out of gear involved crawling under the tractor, never a pleasant task, particularly in the water and mud of a winter wood, and much worse when the rear wheels were dug in and the clearance was reduced. Though owners were not over sensitive to the discomforts endured by their crews the news eventually leaked back to Elworth Works that the arrangement was not a world-beater. However, Fodens at that time were experiencing grave problems in the control of the firm, arising from antagonisms between branches of the family, and the redesign of the winching arrangement to place it above the chassis in a more accessible position was left to other firms. One of the original design of D-types (No.12670) was bought in 1927 by W.R. (Billy) Smith, a sawmiller in a small way, and timber haulier, of Stokenchurch, Bucks. This he called *King of the Forest,* possibly out of deference to its leonine characteristics. It never did a great deal of work for him, preference being given to his Foster Wellington tractor, a more docile and easily controlled machine, though much slower and noisier on the road. In 1930, having apparently tired of the Foden, he sold it to Francis Grover who worked it for some five years before selling it to Boughtons after an accident.

H.& R. Friend of Forest Row, Sussex, had a very similar tractor (No.10992 of 1924) which they used both for furniture removing, and also, with an open trailer wagon, for moving aggregates and road material. The present owner of the firm remarked that his grandfather would never allow more than one trailer behind it so that, as "one of the fierce and powerful", it was chronically underworked and became a financial white elephant. In 1934 Friends sold it to William Brown, a timber haulier newly established in Crowborough, Sussex, after having come down from Yorkshire where he had found it impossibly hard to earn a living. One of the men who came with him was Stan Jacques, who was made mate on the Foden, the driver of which was an older man named Bennett. Bill Brown had secured a contract from John Stenning & Sons of Sheffield Park, Sussex, for the haulage to Sheffield Park of a considerable quantity of round timber, mostly oak, which Stennings had bought at Mereworth, between Tonbridge and Maidstone. The Foden was a very good tool for this work, powerful on the loaded run, and fast on the run back. Mereworth to Sheffield Park is about 36 miles, and the Foden was getting in two trips daily, so that early rising, late nights and no hanging about in between was the order of the day. Whilst running back to Mereworth on one occasion the crankshaft broke in Hadlow Road, Tonbridge, (almost opposite the house where these words are being written), fracturing the steam take-off on the boiler top. Despite having no engine and a cab full of very lively steam, the driver brought it to an orderly stand-still with no damage to anything though with two wheels on the pavement, which prompted a lady to say that "He ought to be locked up!". The remark was overheard by Joe Goodland, who retorted "Locked up? He ought to have a medal!" He towed the Foden back the hundred yards or so to his garage with a 30cwt. Chevrolet, but the little truck was unable to move it up the slope to the workshop. That evening it was pushed up the slope by Charlie Wiles, driving one of the Foden 6-wheeled tar tankers on contract hire from Robert Brett to the South Eastern Tar Distillers who had a works in Tonbridge. Charlie lived in the cul-de-sac behind the author's house, and did the deed under the 'old pals act'.

Fig.115. T.T.Boughton & Sons' Tasker chain drive tractor No. 1830 with what appears to be a massive walnut butt, probably destined for High Wycombe furniture factories. [R.G.Pratt]

Fig.116. Foden No.13232 (1929) was bought by Taylor Bros. in 1932 and ran until 1939. Its load here is an oak butt on a tug with solid rubber tyres.

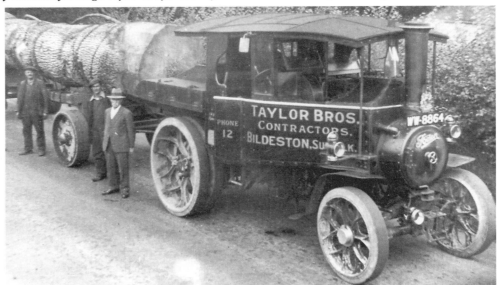

Fig.117. In 1933 H.Judd & Son bought Sentinel No.8777. Harold Judd, leaning by the cab door, drove it himself, and Wally Dell was his mate.

Loads behind the Foden were frequently of the order of 500 Hoppus feet which, with green oak, probably meant about 20 tons plus the weight of the tug. The tug had been converted to solid rubbers using wheels and axles from an old Albion lorry. These made it much easier on the road and able to travel faster. The Foden and this tug were later used to pick up an extremely large elm trunk from a park in West Croydon. After some difficulty it was loaded and the tug was roped out across the grass leaving two very deep ruts in the turf and in a tarmac path that happened to be in the way. Stan protested to his employer that it was too heavy for the tug, but the latter insisted it would be alright. He was a boisterous and impetuous man given to taking chances, which, it must be admitted, usually came off. In this instance he was wrong. On the main London to Eastbourne road, about three miles from the start, and in front of the *Swan & Sugar Loaf* public house, an axle broke, fortunately with the load clear of the tram tracks from the Embankment to Purley which ran past the pub. The firm had just acquired a Latil tractor, with a new timber tug to match it, both on giant pneumatics. This was also hauling timber to Stennings at Sheffield Park, and a phone call to Stennings ensured that when it arrived at the sawmill it was unloaded promptly and sent off to Croydon. As soon as traffic permitted the elm was rolled off the stricken tug and loaded onto the new one to be hauled to Sheffield Park by the Latil. In the meantime Bill Brown had been to Jack Hardwick's scrapyard at Ewell and located an Albion with an axle similar to the broken one on the tug. This was bought, removed from the scrapped lorry, and taken to Croydon. There the tug had already been jacked up and the broken axle unbolted so that the replacement was soon put in. The crew were now into their second day without sleep, having started early the day before and having had no chance since of a decent wash, of taking their clothes off, or even eating more than snack meals. Nevertheless, once the axle was bolted up and the packing removed, the Foden and its crew were off again, this time as far as Frant Station (one station south of Tunbridge Wells on the line to Hastings) where they parked up and at last went home for at least a short night in their own beds. They were still expected to be out again early the next morning!

By the second half of the thirties most, but not all, of the traction engines and road locos had dropped out of timber haulage. A few remained such as the compound Fowler (No.10282) run by the Stowmarket Timber Co. which they kept in service until 1943, but there were not many. Conventional steam tractors were also in full retreat under sheer economic pressure. Whereas the Stowmarket engine was owned by a sawmiller using it for his own work and was part of the general overheads of the mill, most haulage was done under contract on a simple tonnage or ton/mile basis, usually at rock-bottom rates. By about 1936, in the face of competition from internal combustion tractors, and from Fodens, and Sentinels, it had become almost impossible to move swiftly enough with an ordinary steam tractor to clock up a sufficient daily tonnage to get a living even by the combination of 5 o'clock starts and 10 or 11 o'clock finishes. These were the kind of hours being worked by the author's frequently quoted friends, the Newells of Westerham, immediately prior to going over to a diesel tractor. Where piece-work hauliers were working into the same mill as the mill-owner's own tackle, human nature being as it is, they usually got the worst of the jobs or, as it was frequently referred to, the hot end of the poker.

Large numbers of conventional steam tractors were withdrawn from use and scrapped between 1935 and 1939, though the outbreak of war brought a reprieve to several of the survivors. Such was the standing of steam with the timber trade, however, that even as late as October, 1936, the firm of R.T. & J.Hewitt, who traded at Morpeth, Northumberland, bought Sentinel double geared tractor No.9260 new for use in timber hauling. It remained in their hands, though latterly not used, until 1948. Another well-known example of the breed was No.8777, which survived into preservation. Originally delivered to H.Judd & Son of Spencers Wood, near Reading, in July, 1933, and driven by Harold Judd himself with Wally Dell as his mate, it was used in hauling round timber to the Buckinghamshire chair makers. For two years it was on a regular run from Arundel, Sussex, to Princes Risborough, a journey of about 85 miles involving many severe hills and the negotiation of town streets. About eight hours was taken on the journey, and four round trips a week were managed, with five in a good week. With upwards of 600 Hoppus feet of timber on the tug, which had twin pneumatics all round, this was a formidable outfit indeed. The tractor, on giant pneumatics, new and in good condition, was ideal for long distance road work, though many thought the Sentinel somewhat too heavy on the front end for use over soft terrain.

This latter objection had been overcome to a considerable degree in the somewhat earlier No.8369 (for J. & G.Halsey of London Colney, Herts) delivered in 1930, in which the engine was mounted over the rear axle, and the gears, sprocket and winch were all to the rear of the axle, giving a much lighter front axle loading. This tractor came on the end of the solid tyre era. The cab, though roofed fairly generously, was

Fig.118. *An unidentified Bomford & Evershed single cylinder Fowler ploughing engine powering a saw bench. The work appears to be that of further breaking down timber reduced from the round on a rack bench.*
[Bomford collection - MERL]

Fig.119. *Sawing on Viscount Clifden's estate at Whimple. The Yorkshire 5-tonner served as the unit of an articulated timber hauling outfit, a crankshaft extension powering the crude saw bench with its unguarded blade and, apparently, no fast and loose pulleys.* [MERL]

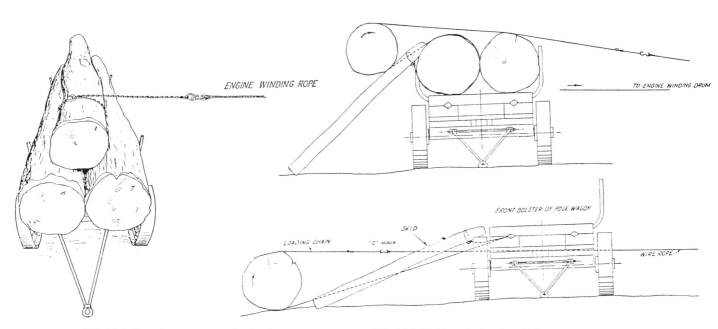

Fig.120. *Turning a tree on the load*
Sketches by G.F.A.Gilbert.

Fig.121. *Rolling timber up skids.*

open at the front and sides and, so far as the riding qualities and crew comfort were concerned, the tractor was much behind Judd's machine, but, on the other hand, it was more suited for local work, loading its own timber. Although not broken up until 1945 the Halsey tractor did very little work in its later years. Judd's tractor was taken over by the Ministry of Works during the war and never went back to timber hauling. The last Sentinel tractor to work timber regularly was probably No.90907 (1933) owned by C.H.James of Kingswinford, Staffordshire. This was used well into the nineteen fifties and fortunately, because its owners were interested in preservation, it has survived.

T.T.Boughton & Sons, with their long tradition of steam operation, were still much involved with steam haulage in the war years but had given up by about 1950, though it was the good luck of the preservation movement that they were very reluctant to break up their Foden timber tractors so that, in consequence, a number survived. Most were conversions from wagons, mounted on pneumatics and fitted with their owners' own design of winch. The most recently restored of the Boughton Fodens are Nos.13476 and 13536. Probably the most exotic item of the Boughton fleet in the pre-war years was the Foden Speed-type tractor No.14044, built in 1931 as a side-tipper for Waddon & Grew of Coleshill, Warwickshire, who used it for hauling roadstone. Boughtons bought it in 1936 and converted it into a tractor. Gordon Hearn of Boughtons once commented that it was capable of 50m.p.h., and it was certainly the most sophisticated item of steam tackle ever to be deployed on timber hauling. When its Foden pistol boiler developed problems the owners replaced it with a Sentinel boiler, but, for whatever reason, it was never quite the same afterwards, and notwithstanding its merits in the way of speed on the road, cab comfort and ease of handling, it was outlived by the rather older overtypes converted from 6-ton wagons, mainly because of the latters' indestructability under rough working.

There have been few descriptions of the round timber trade so detailed and so closely observed as that written by Geoff Gilbert in the R.L.S. Journal;

The Tractor. The usual pattern of engine for timber hauling in later days was the 5-ton tractor, or sometimes the Foden type 'D' or Sentinel tractors. An aspect not generally obvious was the tank capacity; engines with small tanks could well be limited in the amount of roping done at a site with no water handy. It was therefore sometimes necessary to leave without having made a full load. Conversely, an engine with large tanks, such as a Foden or a Sentinel, was often too heavy to get about on soft ground if the tanks were full, and again the output was limited.

The Trailer. According to the part of the country, it was variously known as a timber drag, a timber drug, a timber tug, a timber carriage, or perhaps the most apt description of all, a pole wagon. It was, after all, a steerable forecarriage connected to a hind carriage by a long pole, and formed a development of the underframe of the English farm wagon. Each carriage carried a bolster upon which the load rested, the rear carriage being arranged to move along the pole as required to suit the length of load. A suitable pin registering in holes bored at intervals along the pole fixed the wheelbase once this dimension had been decided upon. The load was retained upon the bolsters by pins, which fitted either into holes bored vertically into the top surfaces, or were attached to the bolster sides by studs and cotters. Ideally the pole was arranged immediately above the axles, thereby providing as much space as possible beneath the load as it lay on the bolsters. In this way there was the least likelihood of the pole becoming damaged by any awkwardly shaped pieces in the load, and the strains of traction were communicated with the minimum bending movement. Some form of braking was provided for the rear carriage and if the vehicle was on steel wheels would comprise the usual pattern of cross-beam with wood shoes pressing against the tyres.

Equipment. A variety of chains for attaching the engine rope to the timber, rolling on the load and binding it in position were always carried. Perhaps both heavy and light chains would be included in a well-run outfit, and ensured that any situation could be dealt with in the most convenient and sure manner. Light loading chains would be about 30 ft. long with 3/8 in. links, while heavier chains would have 7/16 in. or 1/2 in. links. Pulling chains would have 1/2 in. to 3/4 in. links and be up to about 18 ft. long, all chains being fitted with a hook at one end and a ring at the other. At least one 'C' hook or 'S' hook was required and served to couple the eye in the end of the engine rope to the ring end of the chain.

To form an incline from the ground up to the bolsters for loading purposes, two pieces of round timber termed 'skids' were carried. These were some 6 to 10 in. in diameter, according to the strength required, about 8 to 10 ft. in length, and cut from the trunk of a young ash or larch. Other virtually indispensable items were a spare length of wire rope, a snatch block, lifting jack, iron bar, and several scotch blocks. A snatch block was always to be preferred to an ordinary pulley block since it could be opened and slipped into an arrangement of ropes without having to perform any threading 'through' operations.

If the outfit was driven by the owner he would most likely carry a tape and a 'Hoppus' measure, by means of which the cubic contents of every piece in the load could be calculated. Since payment was always based on the number of cubic feet hauled and the mileage covered, these last items were important when the day's earnings had to be reckoned. [The cubic contents of a piece of timber were obtained by squaring the quarter girth measured at mid-length and multiplying it by the length. Hoppus' tables were used as a reckoner to evaluate the result, which was always adopted as the standard in spite of the somewhat generous allowance for waste.]

Dealing with the Timber on the Ground. In most cases it was necessary to move the timber from where it was felled into a suitable position for loading, and at the same time opportunity could be taken to gather together a sufficient number of pieces to make up a full load. If the 'sticks' were small, they might be dragged direct from the engine drawbar, but it was much more often necessary to use the engine winding gear. Ideally a tree would be roped top first, since being lighter this end has less tendency to dig in than the butt, although such a course was often inconvenient in other ways. More often than not, it was the butt end which went first to the accompaniment of much scoring of the turf, although careful work in trimming the end by the fellers could reduce the damage done. The engine was therefore backed to the timber and scotched

Fig.122. *Timber hauling in California sometime between 1895 and 1900, with a Best traction engine double-heading the Holt attached to the loads.*

Fig.123. *John Young's well-known Foden engine (No.4752) in Chris Lambert's upper yard at Horsmonden on June 20, 1953, when it was still a working engine.* [W.S.Love]

up at a distance away in keeping with the length of wire rope on the drum. If the conditions would not allow the engine to come within range, then the spare length of wire rope had to pressed into service and arranged in tandem. The rope was never attached to the tree direct, since it quickly became damaged by such treatment, and use was always made of one of the short chains and 'C' hook. Once scotched up firmly, the engine could begin winding, although particularly in the woods care had to taken that the moving 'stick' did not collide with any objects hidden in the undergrowth or with standing timber. It might be necessary to reset the direction of the rope pull to achieve this object at times and the judicious use of the iron bar by the mate could often prevent trouble. After slackening off the rope, the 'stick' would be prised sideways and a fresh pull then attempted, but large and heavy pieces of timber could require the use of the snatch block attached carefully to a standing tree by means of a short chain. Best practice demanded an old sack to be wrapped around the chain to prevent the bark being damaged by the links, but worst practice would run the rope round the tree with no pulley at all. According to the distance to the loading site and the length of rope on the winding drum, the engine might have to reset several times. In this connection the provision of a slip pattern winding drum was a great time-saver, since the rope could be paid out as the engine travelled forward. A fixed drum meant that the rope had to be drawn in and secured to the drum after each pull and the engine then moved forward the correct distance, which would be paced out by the mate. The rope was then run out again and re-attached to the 'stick'. The pieces of timber forming the load would be carefully drawn up with the butt ends in line and arranged if possible in the order in which they would naturally lay together on the bolsters.

Setting the Engine for Winding. The ability of an engine to haul on its winding rope depended not only upon the power developed but also on the ability to resist being drawn backwards. The exact method of 'scotching up' depended upon conditions, the practice permitted by the owner and the type of engine involved. A suitable large block behind each of the hind wheels would hold quite a lot, but the greatest resistance had to be provided at the side where the winding drum was situated. When the conditions were soft, blocks would soon push into the ground and quite an amount of packing would be needed before results became effective. Sometimes a spud would be put on at the back of the wheel in an effort to transfer the pull into a downward thrust on to the scotch and so prevent it moving back. A favourite method with a 5-ton tractor was to chain the bottom of the wheel at the winding drum side to the drawbar, and lay a piece of timber about 6 in. square and 3 ft. long, over the chain and under the wheel. As the engine ran backwards a little, it mounted on the timber, pressing it into the ground, and at the same time the chain became taut, thus forming a most effective anchor. Naturally, this method caused damage to the paintwork and tended to buckle the tank side plate, but many engines bore the scars of this treatment to their last day. When very heavy roping was to be done, the front of the engine was often chained to a suitable fixed object, such as a tree stump or, if the forester was not about, to a standing tree. Tell-tale marks in the bark would often bear silent witness that the timber hauliers had been that way and had difficulty in anchoring the engine down. If there were two sets of tackle at work together one engine could be used to hold the other, or both ropes used together. By incorporating a snatch block into the system, with a return rope, the effective pull could be nearly doubled, although at half speed and over half the distance. Anchorage for the return rope could be to the engine drawbar, or a nearby fixed object. Many engines pulled best if set at a slight angle to the rope in spite of the extra weight put on the guide rollers, and tended to slew round into this position as they took the strain.

Loading. The pieces forming the load, having been drawn into line, were then ready for winding up the skids. If not already in position, the pole wagon was now brought parallel to the 'sticks' but sufficiently far away to allow the skids to be set up. Depending on the length of the timber, the pole wagon might require opening or shutting, i.e. lengthening or shortening, at this time. If the timber was long and the carriage opened right out, it would be placed so that the load would come well forward on the bolster, with only a minimum clearance to the rear of the engine when coupled up. In this way the loading of the fore and hind carriage was equalised as far as possible, the heavy butt ends balancing the thinner and lighter but longer overhang of the tops at the rear. The bolster pins at the loading side were then removed and the skids put in place, their lower ends resting on the ground and the upper ends on the tops of the wheels. The engine would then be set up at right angles to the pole, roughly opposite the mid-point between the bolsters and sufficiently far away to keep the loading chains clear of the rope rollers. A typical 'run' for each loading chain would be to start at the ring end with the formation of a noose, which was drawn tight around the top end of the skid. The chain was then passed to the other end of the bolster, either round a bolster stay or through a ring specially provided for the purpose. From here it was led back inside the skid under the 'stick' to be loaded and returned to a point midway between the bolsters where both chains were coupled to the engine winding rope by the 'C' hook. Any adjustment in chain length necessary to obtain an even pull was made by a knotted loop in either or both chain ends, but better practice provided grab hooks, i.e. hooks with a specially shaped opening which would readily engage back into the links when the loop was formed. The engine then wound the timber up the skids and on to the bolsters, and since two principles of mechanical advantage were employed, that is, an inclined plane, and a virtual arrangement of a pulley, the pull required was not usually excessive. However, if the load comprised one single but very large piece, conditions could be rather more difficult. By careful chain adjustment an even pull could be obtained which caused the 'stick' to roll up the skids parallel to the pole, but if there was a tendency to go skew, it meant lowering back for a fresh start. As far as possible, loading was carried out 'uphill' to guard against the possibility of a runaway across the bolsters, which could well turn the carriage over. Once the 'sticks' forming the bottom of the load had filled the width of the bolsters, the pins were replaced and the skids and chains reset to the last piece loaded. Sometimes if a load was made up of a number of smaller pieces, the top ones could well be wound up without the skids, since, as the load became higher, their inclination became too steep to be of much assistance. As the various pieces came into place on the load it was frequently necessary to prise these into place with the crowbar or even turn them a little so that their natural irregularities would accommodate each other. This turning was effected by passing a short chain around the 'stick' in such a manner that a gentle pull on the engine winding rope caused it to rotate without moving it sideways.

Once the load was made it was tightly secured in position by binding chains, which were passed round the sticks and anchored to the bolsters. The binding chains could be chains kept specially for this purpose, but very often the loading chains were used. To draw the binding chains tight and keep them that way a flexible stick about 3 in. in diameter and some 10 ft. long , and called a 'gob stick' or 'lever stick' was used [They were also known as 'wresting bats'. R.A.W.]. One end of this stick was inserted into the binding chain and pulled down to form a twist, tourniquet fashion, while the other end was secured by a light chain to a suitable part of the carriage. Since the stick was pulled into a bow it acted as a spring in keeping the chain tight and would allow for any small variations in length due to the load settling. In later days some hauliers used 'chain jacks' or 'chain dogs' and, particularly if an old piece of boiler tube was slipped over the handle for extra leverage, a considerable degree of tension could be obtained. There was, however, a lack of springiness with them, and when examined at the first stop for water they could usually be taken up a link or two. Any spare equipment, skids, etc., were next loaded up and preparation made for the haul to the road.

To the Road. If the ground conditions were suitable the engine could be coupled up direct to the pole wagon and made to draw the load to the highway, the distance being anything from a few yards to perhaps half a mile, and across several fields. It was surprising how different surfaces affected adhesion; dry ploughed land provided a good grip for solid rubber tyres, but of course the going was heavy. A large clump of bluebells in flower would soon stop a rubber-tyred engine since the sap issuing from the crushed stems was particularly slimy. If the surface was firm but greasy, the spuds would be used, but as soon as the carriage wheels began to cut in, it was necessary to start roping. Careful selection of the exact route often assisted in the avoidance of the softest places into which the load could easily sink to the axles, sometimes making pulling the load off, and a fresh start the only solution. Once more, when roping a loaded carriage it was often necessary to change the direction of the pull, especially if there were many obstructions along the route or a bad side hill existed. The usual fixed objects were again sought in order that the snatch block could be put into use. Sometimes the most awkward part was the exit through the last gateway and on to the road, there often being insufficient room to rope all the way. Yet when the engine was coupled up it would refuse to turn when pulling hard and head for the opposite hedge. Again hedge roots, tree stumps, gateposts, etc., were all considered as an anchorage for the snatch block. Many times the most frail and unlikely looking hedge root would provide the solution, yet a most substantial tree stump would disintegrate when a strain was put on it. Generally short pulls were preferable among obstructions since the tendency of the carriage to deviate from the desired course was reduced to a minimum by this procedure.

On the Road. Once out and coupled up, a check would be made to ensure that nothing was left behind; after all tomorrow's work could be miles away, and why leave good equipment about for others to find and use? Ideally the chains would be carried in boxes on the engine or carriage, but mostly they were coiled up in bundles and hung off various places on the vehicles. These bundles resembled great clusters of grapes which swung to and fro as the outfit trundled along. If provision was made for working the trailer brakes as on a Foden or Sentinel tractor, it was connected up, suitable adjustments being made to the operating cable if the carriage had been opened or shut. Probably the most noticeable thing on the road was the way in which the pole wagon wanted to take charge of the engine, both for direction and speed. With the considerable weight on the forecarriage it became difficult to lock round, such that there was a marked reluctance to change direction. Every change of gradient was felt, particularly with a 5-ton tractor, and an apparently flat road became a downhill, which caused a rapid increase of speed, or an uphill which required change of gear. This matter was hardly surprising, since in most cases the engine was being expected to haul twice its own weight. With a long load and the carriage opened right out to the full wheelbase - probably about 18 to 20 feet - great care had to be taken in turning sharp corners. Not only did the full lock on the forecarriage render the load unstable at the front end and liable to turn over, but the hind carriage naturally followed a much smaller radius than the engine. The practice of moving over to the right-hand side of the road before making a left-hand turn must have confused many other road users who, no doubt, thought the driver must have just left the 'local'. If there was a long back overhang, the tail end had a nasty habit of demolishing signposts and other roadside objects on the outside of a sharp turn. Care with the application of trailer brakes, if these were worked from the engine, was necessary since slack in the drawgear could cause a considerable amount of lost motion in the mechanism which was suddenly taken up as the shoes began to bite and gave a nasty snatch. Negotiation of sharp curves also affected the operation of cable-worked brakes and made their operation uncertain. Many operators relied on the engine to hold the load down the easier hills, and let the mate get off to turn the brake wheel on the carriage itself when steeper descents were involved. Any high-speed running on rough roads, whether by design or accident, could well upset a load of awkward shaped pieces since the springs on most pole wagons - if there were any - became inoperative with a heavy load. Usually the lifting jack and bar could put things right, but in one instance on record the snatch block and engine rope had to be used in conjunction with the overhanging bough of a large oak to reset one of the pieces in the load.

Unloading. Many sawmills had a crane of some sort for unloading the timber and placing it on the stockpile or the saw carriage, and this operation was thus fairly straightforward. Often the most difficult part was getting the load under the crane, which was frequently not of the travelling pattern. It always seemed to involve backing the outfit in the limited space among the piles of timber. Many drivers could not back a trailer and the favourite drill was to go forward under the crane, unload and then manhandle the carriage out. Sometimes, if the crane was steam or electric, its driver could be persuaded to lift the carriage up clear, turn it around in mid-air and put it down after the engine had backed out. It is to be admitted that many mill yards were inches deep in bark, sawdust, and other rubbish, making the pushing back of a loaded carriage somewhat difficult. Where a crane was not available, the load would be barred off, or pulled off with the engine winding rope, perhaps using the skids if required.

Conclusion. As with other trades employing steam engines, timber hauliers' tackle varied considerably, much of it being somewhat ramshackle equipment severely battered by ruthless handling. Sometimes a well-kept set would be found, operated by a careful owner who was particular about appearances. The work was arduous and taxed both men and machines severely; loading chains were up to 1cwt. each, and the larger skids 2 cwt., weights which confirm that considerable physical strength was required by the crew. With this physical strength a great deal of skill was necessary if the work was to be carried out satisfactorily and with no mishaps or breakages. There was no economy in running with constant repair bills for breakages due to carelessness, and even less if the bills were for damage to property. The fact that the timber might be felled in a wood, a field, a park, or even on the lawns of a stately home, ensured that there was a great variety of situations with no two days' work exactly alike. Timber hauling did not suit everybody, but for those who liked open-air life, working with an engine and travelling beyond one's own parish, it was more attractive than going threshing. The experiences gained at timber hauling are not readily forgotten, and when the limitations of the tackle are considered in relation to present-day equipment, the activities of these little engines and the men who drove them seem all the more remarkable.

Chapter 7

Steam on the Fairground

The nature of the fairground underwent a transformation in the middle years of the last century with the arrival of the large steam powered riding machines. Until the eighteen sixties a fair had been largely made up of what would now be termed side-stuff - hooplas, fit-up theatres, puppet shows, wrestling, boxing and juggling booths, exhibitions of freaks and monstrosities, and dancing bears, together with food vendors of all sorts, selling cakes, gingerbreads, ginger-pop, hot potatoes, brandy snaps, coconut ice, stickjaw toffee, humbugs, hot pies, jellied eels, cockles, winkles and oysters. Early riding machines, perhaps the equivalent in size of a modern juvenile, were light and relatively easy to transport. Many of the items of those days were capable of being carried on the back of their owner or, if not on his unaided, on those of himself and his wife. Many more travellers made do with a barrow, a pack animal or a light horse-drawn cart or van. The advent of railways had introduced some possibilities of variation. Instead of walking from gaff to gaff the packman could take the train although the fare was often the obstacle. Lack of resources, both capital and revenue, was endemic on fairgrounds. Many travellers lived hand-to-mouth by the use of sharp wits and dogged endurance.

The arrival of riding machines driven by steam changed the image of the fairground from that of a rather tired, decaying mediæval survival into that of up-to-date entertainment. Besides this they introduced a new type of showman with a considerable capital tied up in them, and they posed new problems in transport. The centre of a steam roundabout made a heavy load for horses, with the other packing trucks nearly as heavy. For a while all were horse-hauled. The railway, an obvious alternative, was expensive and unaccommodating and, in consequence, used sparingly although on the Continent, where the loading gauge was more generous, showmen seemed to get on rather better with the use of rail transport. The characteristic Continental showman's vehicle was and is, even today, longer, lower, and roofed in more pronounced ellipses than that of his British counterpart to suit the restrictions of railway transport. In England most fairground moves continued to be made by road and, for the time being, by horses. Horse establishments of twenty to thirty horses were not uncommon, each horse having to be fed twice daily, leaving its quota of dung and urine, requiring shoeing and grooming, and being subject to the periodic epizootics which plagued the horse world, besides the lesser chills and coughs to which intermittently worked horses were prone.

To the showman with first-hand experience of steam as the propulsive force for a ride, its attraction as a means of haulage for his loads on the road was strong. It seems clear that the first uses of steam haulage for fairground purposes were by hiring traction engines. Though there is practically no documentary evidence for this assertion the oral evidence for it is considerable from both sides of the transaction. The engines that were hired must, in the ordinary way, have been general purpose engines, the role of which in road haulage has already been discussed. The development of the road locomotive, as the term was later understood, came after the use of hired traction engines by fairground machine proprietors began. By the eighties some fairground people had begun to purchase their own engines. Because records of changes of engine ownership at this period are not complete it behoves one not to be too categorical, but examples can be cited, such as William Irvin's *Pride of Bucks* (Burrell 8NHP general purpose single No.1636) or the two duplex cylinder Savages (Nos.228 and 229 of 1880 and 1881 respectively), the first supplied to W.Sanger and the second to George Twigdon. Twenty years later No.228 was the victim of the explosion of its firebox when it was owned by John Beach and working at a fair at Alexandra Palace, North London. This incident was the subject of some very good detective work and an interesting article by Roger West in *STEAMING* of Summer, 1986. The accident happened on the Saturday of the 1901 August Bank Holiday fair about 8p.m. John Beach had lit the engine up about 6p.m. to be ready for driving lights at dusk, and as it came up to working pressure there was a failure of several stays on the right-hand side of the firebox. As a result of this the plate was pulled over the remaining stays. Most of the force went downwards digging a hole some three feet deep, and the smokebox door was blown some distance. No one was killed and few were injured, but the driver, George Musk, lost two fingers. Beach had had the engine three years and had bought it from Savages, taking their word for it that it was in good order, but the subsequent inquiry established that it must have had some broken stays and many more badly wasted at the time of the sale.

Fig.124. Nottingham Goose Fair in 1907 when steam was at its peak and all the major machines were driven and hauled by steam. The Pat Collins machines occupy centre stage (his Golden Cockerels and Motors) with Reuben Holdsworth's slip (to the right).

Fig.125. Showmans' haulage by general purpose engine. Fowler No.3013 (1876) Lightning hauling Emerson & Hazard's Leaping Horses loads.
[Charles H.Dean collection]

Fig.126. Fowler official photo of their No.4922, the traction centre built for J.Crampton of Leeds in 1885. This lasted until 1927.

120

At a first glance it seems an obvious step for all travellers to have gone from hiring to owning haulage engines. In practice it is not so obvious. Despite the spread of steam worked riding machines the travellers of the eighties were essentially horse people, well versed in the vagaries of horse behaviour and characteristics and the practical management of horses, but not yet so used to owning or managing engines. This is not to say that they were necessarily humane or sentimental horse owners, though some were, but as master men they knew at least as much about equine management as the horsemen they employed. This enabled them to keep tight control and to see through subterfuges and dodges. With an engine it was different. Not many understood or cared much about the traction engine. Consequently, when they owned one, they were much more in the hands of their paid engine drivers, and might find themselves at a disadvantage, a position no master showman relished. With a hired engine, on the other hand, the control of it was someone else's worry. Furthermore the acquisition of an engine meant another commitment of capital which might already be pledged up to or beyond the acceptable limit on the riding machine. Finally came the fact that a haulage engine owned by the machine proprietor himself was, like the horses, idle when it was not on the road, leading to under-use of an expensive asset though, on the credit side, ownership saved the cost of hiring and, once a good driver was found to manage and maintain the engine, the owner was independent of outside help. Independence is valuable to most people other than the inveterate scrounger and many show people value it almost to the point of fanaticism. It is a difficult thing to evaluate in cash terms but a thing to be prized, nevertheless.

The conception of combining the centre truck of the ride, a heavy and indivisible load for horses, with a haulage engine had a classic simplicity, saving at a stroke the idleness of the engine whilst the ride was built up and yet conferring on the riding master the advantage of steam haulage under his own ownership. This is how the late W.Michael Salmon summed up the story of the twenty or so traction centres that were built:

"... At one stroke the heavy, high and unstable centre truck was gone, the expense of the separate engine was saved, and whilst the whole of the conventional ride might be a bit too much for one engine on unpaved roads, the traction centre could tow the remainder of the ride behind it. ....

Basically the arrangement consisted of an upward and forward extension of the hornplates of a traction engine to form a turret of such a height that the cheese wheel of a roundabout could be mounted on it, complete, in the case of the gallopers, with the bevel gearing for the drive to the horse cranks. The drive could be by a vertical shaft from the crankshaft, comparable to that of a ploughing engine the other way up, or it could be by a separate steam engine mounted on the turret. A small vertical, or in some cases horizontal, engine was also provided to drive the organ, in the same way as the 'model' on the smokebox of a conventional centre engine.

When the ride was built up, the traction centre had to be driven up on to the gantries, similar to, but heavier than, [the weight of these gantries was a great snag. (R.A.W)] those for a normal centre truck in order to give the required height for the ride, and of course, once there, the engine was no longer available for shunting the empty trucks, or any other purpose. All the extra gear made the engine extremely heavy and in the case of a gallopers centre, top-heavy. This would be less marked in the case of a switchback centre owing to the absence of the galloper bevels, but even so, an R.L.S. member [the late Fred Barker] with some experience of these engines stated that he never heard of this extra top weight causing any difficulty on the road.

A well-known series of pictures shows the Savage traction centre owned by Charles Abbott in a ditch, but it is understood that this happened when the engine was passing its own loads in a narrow road, and in the circumstances any engine might have done the same thing. She came out again with the help of a team of timber horses and some pulleys. This engine was a switchback engine, however. Traction centres have also been condemned for being very slow on the road. As many of them were built in the 1880's, this is hardly surprising, and it is illogical to compare their performance on the road with that of a three-speed loco built thirty years later.

Among the builders of this type of engine we would expect to find Savages of Kings Lynn in the lead. In 1880 Frederick Savage filed a Patent [No.3937] relating to traction centres in which two forms were illustrated and described. That which was eventually adopted in practice must have been a combination of the two, for the patent allowed for a turret over the hornplates, entirely over the firebox, and a drive by friction wheels. The other shows a turret mounted over the smokebox, so that the chimney could go straight up the middle. Drive in this case was a vertical shaft and bevel wheels. A modified form of 'dynamo bracket' attached low down on the smokebox carried a 'musical organ' across the front of the engine. Just how the unfortunate driver was to see where he was going on the road, or how he was to sweep his tubes, is not explained. Nevertheless, this design contains the germ of the later centre trucks used for switchbacks, with the boiler along the length of the truck.

With the ink on the Patent scarcely dry, Savage built two 8NHP double cylinder traction centres in 1880/81 for W.Sanger and G.Twigdon.

Savage's Works were never very large, and at that date they were very busy with the new rides, so it seems that they took a batch of eight 6NHP single cylinder engines from J.& H.McLaren of Leeds in 1880 or 1881, to which they added the roundabout gear and the rest of the ride. These were McLaren Nos. 72, 95 to 100 inclusive, and 103. They subsequently took at least two more from the same makers.

Meanwhile John Fowler & Co. had built their No.4922 of 1885 for J.Crampton of Leeds, and this was fitted with a turret which appears to owe much to the Savage design. Fowlers subsequently described this as a 'Whirligig Engine' in their catalogues. This survived until 1927, and we have an eye-witness account of one of its last fairs by the late

F.W.Barker. It had no canopy, it drove the ride off the main engine, and had a small engine on the side of the smokebox to drive the organ.

On the other side of Thetford Chase, Frederick John Burrell of St.Nicholas Works was giving the matter some thought, and his patent was lodged in November of 1895. By this time electric light had come into more common use and the mounting of a dynamo at the front of an engine became accepted practice. The Burrell patent (No.21 403) was intended to use the engine as a centre engine without losing it as a generator as well. Thus to a turret not dissimilar to the Savage type he added a pair of cylinders up above the driver's head to drive the cheese wheel, leaving the main engine to drive the dynamo. So far as is known no engine was built new to this specification but a single crank compound owned by George Baker of Southampton was converted to this system. It is said that with the main engine running the dynamo, the little organ engine on the side of the smokebox working, and the two cylinders "up in the roof of the cab" driving the cheese wheel, it took a good man to keep steam in her. This arrangement did take cognisance of the fact that the main engine of a traction was too big for driving a ride, and also for the fact that the need for a reverse did not arise.

It was common practice to work main-engine traction centres at a reduced pressure when running the ride, and of course they could be, and it is said that sometimes they were, made to run backwards. Whilst this could be a questionable joke on the patrons in the case of a set of gallopers, it would be dangerous on a switchback, where some unfortunate and unplanned stresses could be set up in the Sullivans; for the cars were supposed to be towed, and not pushed.[Michael's dynamics were at fault here. The pulling irons would have suffered the unplanned stresses. (R.A.W.)]

At least one other Burrell was converted to a traction centre for use with a three-abreast, but when Henry Thurston had his set new in 1887, it had a Richard Hornsby engine, No.6292, the only example of a traction centre attributed to this firm. It was a compound, and had Aveling wheels of spring type, when new, but by 1921 had been converted to an ordinary road engine."

Despite this qualified success of traction centres some of the principal showmen began to turn to purpose-built straight showmen's engines. Just as a well-to-do showman of earlier times would have prided himself on the quality of his horses so it seems likely that a leader in machines might also want to be a pace-setter in the use of road engines. The facts concerning the early purpose-built Burrell showmen's engines have already been extensively researched by historians of authority. It seems almost beyond any reasonable doubt that the first to be constructed specifically for show business use, though not for ownership by a showman, was Burrell No.1287 of 1887, an 8NHP single for William Shipley of Driffield, Yorks, who hauled Wellburn's gallopers by contract. This doughty old engine, which worked for forty-five years, was essentially a road haulage engine with certain added features. After being used for some years in its original form it was converted into a traction centre engine by Reynolds & King. By the 1920's it was owned by Morley Brothers of Castleford, Yorks, and worked until 1932.

The second built was the famous No.1451, *Monarch*, for Jacob Studt of Maesteg, delivered on December 21, 1889, also an 8NHP single but with dynamo bracket and dynamo. Studt was a man of pioneering spirit both in his riding machines and his engine. With *Monarch* he had sized up the commercial value of being able to light his show by electricity, but in fact, he did not keep the engine very long, and by the autumn of 1891 it had passed to Hengler & Matthews of Taynton, Gloucestershire. Thereafter it had four further known owners before it disappeared from view in 1912. When Studt next bought a Burrell in 1896 it was the single crank compound (No.1909) named *Majestic*. After five years he sold this engine also. The later Burrells he owned were double crank compounds.

One more single cylinder Burrell showman's engine was built, the 7NHP No.1470 (delivered on March 15, 1890) for G.& J.Bartlett of Fordingbridge, Hants, and named *Pride of the South*. With their unique set of galloping horses, reputed to have been built by Vosper of Portsmouth, it was a familiar sight on Wessex fairgrounds until the early twenties. As a matter of interest the Bartletts were later the owners of Jacob Studt's second Burrell *Majestic* (No.1909) after he had sold it. After the three single cylindered showmen's engines Burrells turned to compounds, initially on their single crank arrangement, of which they built thirty-three. With No.1971 (February, 1897), however, they began building the double crank compound type for which they became celebrated.

The Fowler contribution to the ranks of showmen's engines up to the end of the nineteenth century was very slight by comparison with Burrells'; a total of eighteen - four singles and the remainder compounds - whereas the Burrell total was 45.

Since each ride had its own centre engine, the primary function of the road engines remained that of hauling the loads on the road and shunting them on the fairground. There were a few promotionally acute showmen, such as Jacob Studt, who went in for electric light and who were prepared to buy a road locomotive equipped to run it, though a few others compromised by using portable electric light engines. The greatest impetus to the multiplication of showmen's engines came from the development of the moving picture business manifested in the proliferation of travelling temporary cinemas or bioscope

Fig.127. Burrell No.1470 (1890) Pride of the South, owned by G.& J.Bartlett of Fordingbridge, Hants. A 7NHP, it was the last new single cylinder engine to be built for a showman.

Fig.128. Winding up the centre truck of George Irvin's Savage Gallopers onto the trams by the wire rope from his Foster Marvel *in the background.*

Fig.129. (below) J.Matthews' Fowler No.13047 (1914) The Wanderer *was a War Department engine, converted by Charles Openshaw. The lettering and lining was probably the work of Tommy Matthews, who died in July, 1987.*

shows, either on fairgrounds or independently. Bioscope shows in the mid-nineties were primitive in their tenting, and gas lit as to their projection equipment, but quickly developed into elaborate travelling cinemas with organ fronts, padded seats, and electric light in the projectors and auditoria, a most marked improvement in both the practical and safety aspects. With inflammable film even electricity was a potential hazard, but to a much lesser degree than gas.

'Bioscope' was the trade name of the Warwick Trading Co. Ltd. of 3/4 Warwick Court, Holborn, London, founded by an American, Charles Urban, to supply films, cine cameras, projection equipment, and other requisites to the trade. When the Boer War broke out Urban, with characteristic enterprise, sent a reporter named Rosenthal to South Africa to film on the spot. As the camera weighed about 15cwt. and had to be mounted by a ladder, the films were neither very spontaneous nor very close to the front line, but they were a thousand times in advance of the fake war films made by a trade rival on a rocky piece of ground near Blackburn. Bioscope shows appeared, proliferated, reached their peak, and died in the space of about twenty years, but from 1900 to 1914, when their influence was highest, they provided the largest market for showmen's engines. It could be said that the availability of the showman's engine capable of providing the motive power on the road and the electrical power on the site had made this flowering of the bioscope shows possible. This combination of functions on the engines had been made possible, in its turn, by Dr.Hopkinson's invention of the modern carbon brush dynamo in 1886. A pioneer builder of such dynamos was F.W.Dickinson. Who first had the idea of putting such a generator on a dynamo bracket on the smokebox of a road locomotive is more in the chicken and egg category. Did it originate with Burrells or with their customer, Jacob Studt?

The demise of the travelling bioscope shows, because of the emergence of the static cinema, threw a good many engines onto the market. At the end of the war came the disposal of many of the heavy road locomotives owned by the War Department of which a substantial proportion were converted to fairground use. Two firms active in this field were Charles Openshaw of Reading, Berkshire, and James Graven & Sons of Ely, Cambridgeshire, but they were not alone. The War Stores Disposal Board also sold off a considerable stock of steam tractors and wagons. These, also, were taken up widely by showmen. There were, besides, thousands of lorries put onto the market, the arrival of which came a little after the demobilisation of the men who had learned to drive them in the forces. The effect of these events was to encourage self-sufficiency in transport amongst many travellers who would never have aspired to the ownership of an engine in pre-war days.

It must be remembered that, at any time, only a well-to-do elite of showmen were in a sufficient way of business to be able to command the ready cash or the credit which would enable them to order new engines. Even then it was sometimes a struggle that demanded great personal frugality. The story is told that Burrell No.3910, *Wait and See,* got its name because about the time that it had become known that it was on order its intending owners, Crowther & Johnson of Leeds, whilst having a meal in an eating-house, overheard a conversation on the other side of a high-backed settle discussing their intended purchase and demanding rhetorically to know how they were going to pay for it. The story may be apocryphal but it has a ring of truth.

In pre-1914 days, owners of lesser rides, unable to afford new engines, had perforce either to make do with what the second-hand market provided, to continue with horses, or to hire. But even those well enough off to purchase and use new engines did not necessarily forsake hiring altogether. For example, Anderton & Rowlands continued to hire Parsons' *John Bull* at least until the 1914-18 war; Jack Rundle of New Bolingbroke was doing haulage by contract for Frank Sedgwick and other showmen in the early twenties, and Brunsdons of Stonehouse, Gloucestershire, were still hauling for Whites into the 1930's using, by that time, a 'D'-type Foden.

The 1914-18 war had dealt a double blow to civilian use of horses. Whilst the war was on horses were scarce and dear, and horse feed very expensive. Its aftermath flooded the market with cheap lorries and steam tractors. During this period many travelling families who hitherto had stuck to horses went straight over to motors. Others used ex-Ministry of Munitions steam wagons or tractors. Billy Mayne, for example, worked Garrett 4CD tractor No.33325 (1918). After the war a few German Kemna traction engines arrived in this country and even one of these found its way into fairground use in the ownership of Sam Brumby as a haulage engine, unadorned by a dynamo.

Fig.130. Foden No.737, delivered in March, 1904, to John Ogden of Liverpool, in time for the 1904 travelling season, was not only the first purpose-built showman's wagon but probably the first wagon of any sort to be used by a showman.

Fig.131. Twelve years later Foden No.6586 (1916) was bought by Joe Fletcher (standing between the wagon and the trailer). After the war it was sold to Tommy Essam.

Fig.132. Probably the first purpose-built showman's tractor was Garrett No.24063 for another Cardiff showman, John Studt. It was the first Garrett compound tractor to be delivered, though the second to be ordered.

American FWD (Four Wheel Drive) lorries were popular with showmen. With drive on both axles they were useful for getting on to and off of awkward or wet sites. The other stand-by of the showmen was the second-hand Tilling Stevens petrol electric bus which could, by a little surgery on its electrical arrangements, be made to double up nicely as a generating vehicle for lights and driving a smaller ride. These old buses became available during the twenties and some lasted into the nineteen fifties. Indeed the very last of the Tillings petrol electrics known to the author to have worked on a fairground was that owned by George Pickard of Ashford, Middlesex, which was in use until the mid-sixties.

As we have seen a number of showmen went in for overtype steam wagons which they either used as such or converted to tractors. Some went further and bought new; A.J.Peters of Worcester had Foden No.11400 in 1924 turned out as a showman's wagon; Phil Case of Swansea had his Foden (No.13250 of 1929) new, or at least as an ex-demonstrator, complete with brass olivers and dynamo. Contrary to fairground practice with steam it had a right-hand flywheel and dynamo pulley. Though Foden tractors had a following in the 1930's, such as John Beach's No.12462 (new in 1927) which he had from 1934 to 1947, the majority of tractors used on fairgrounds were conventional compound tractors. The Garrett 4CD had many adherents - a few bought new, such as John Studt's No.26063, the first ever delivered though actually the second one made, No.27342 of 1909 built to accompany Charles Hewson's bioscope show, or No.31025 of 1912 supplied to Tommy Cotterell whose permanent address was Droitwich but who, at the time he purchased the engine, had a fit-up cinema within a stone's throw of Garretts' works at Leiston. Because bioscope shows had such a brief period of popularity the fate of Tommy Cotterell's is common to many. In 1914 a local syndicate built a fixed cinema in Leiston and his public deserted him. Other bioscope proprietors sensing the change afoot transferred their energies to the static cinema. President Kemp, for instance, built one in Earlstown, Newton-le-Willows, that was considered palatial in its time. By the end of the 1914-18 war the bioscope business had been abandoned by all but a few diehards.

The last Garrett delivered new to a showman was *Medina* (No.33902) sold to James Humphries of Pelsall, Staffordshire, in 1920, and later owned by Charles Presland. By the late 1930's the tide was running against tractors but *Medina* was not laid off until 1946, saved by the war. Garrett tractors delivered new to showmen were outnumbered many times over by those which reached the trade second or third-hand from civilian or War Department sources.

Burrell engines of all kinds were held in good esteem by fairground people. Some Burrell tractors were delivered new of which No.2982 (1908) sold to Walter Payne of Dartford and No.3185 (1910) supplied to Purchase Bros. of Deptford, London, and named *Wallace*, may be cited as samples, but a good many more were taken into it as used engines in the decade after the first war. After 1927 when the 'Construction & Use' regulations were amended so as to make steel wheels all but impossible for road haulage purposes the Burrell tractor declined in popularity because the closeness of the end of the crankshaft to the offside rear wheel made it difficult to fit a bolt-on rubber to the full width of the wheel. Some, however, had a very long life with showmen, notably William Beach's *May Queen* (No.3497 of 1913) which continued with him, and after him, with his daughter Sally, until 1950, latterly with the front end on pneumatics.

Fowler tractors were also esteemed but since fewer were made than Avelings or Garretts, for instance, they were relatively sparser on the fairground. A well-known example at East Anglian and London Section fairs was Allan Downs's No.14412 which, unlike his larger Fowler, No.10282, the last big Fowler to be converted for use by a showman, survived into preservation days. Several people used Aveling & Porter tractors. James Sanders, of Ash, Kent, had No.6093, afterwards owned by Ernest Aldridge of Snodland, Kent. The one with the most tragic history was No.7414, *The Rising Sun*, owned by Frank Turner and his wife Jessie (née Beach). Whilst it was generating light at Neasden on July 18, 1935, with Frank on the footplate, he was struck and killed by a bullet carelessly fired from a shooter nearby. Jessie continued to travel after his death and kept the engine at work for several years. When she ceased to use it she had it parked up in the yard at Hayes in memory of Frank. To anyone who tried to buy it for preservation she used to say that she would keep it until she died, and that under the terms of her will it would then be broken up but, in fact, she had not stipulated anything so drastic, and after she died in 1978 it was sold into preservation.

Fig.133. Fowler No. 10323 (1905) was sold new to John Studt of Cardiff who named it after the then popular Japanese Admiral Togo, but after it passed to White Bros. they renamed it The Welsh Horse. Here it is seen in the yard of John Allen & Son at Cowley after an extensive repair and repaint.

Fig.134. Its companion in the White stable was Burrell No.3715 (1916) which they had new, here seen also in the yard at Cowley. Additionally the Whites had cartage done for them by Brunsdons of Stroud, Gloucester.
[Figs.133 and 134; Basil Harley]

Most tractor makers got a look in somewhere on the the fairground. There were a few Ransomes such as No.20674 (1908) owned by Mrs.Smart, of Ealing, for a year or two but it was an early casualty and was cut up about 1930. The Ruston & Proctor, a rarity amongst tractors in that it had four shafts, was rarely seen, though Connelly Brothers of Blackpool had No.52551 for a while in the mid-thirties. It was said, somewhat unkindly, that Rustons would hardly have sold any tractors at all had there not been a Ministry of Munitions order for ninety. The McLaren, another four-shafter, also appeared as a very rare bird on fairgrounds. Most were ex-War Department. Again the Savage *Little Samson* tractor, product of a firm famed for its riding machines, had a very thin representation. Claytons and Marshalls were other scarce breeds. The Tasker was a well-known and highly respected make of tractor, handy and reliable and a good steamer, but again not common. George Irvin & Sons' No.1786, a chain drive tractor, was seen on the fairgrounds of London and the nearer parts of the Home Counties until the post-war years but succumbed to motors along with their two big Fosters immediately after the war. The other Hampshire make, the Wallis & Steevens, had a limited but steady clientele among showmen. The Pelhams had a pair of them, and for a while W.Symonds had *Nobby* No.7393 (1913). This had spent twenty-five years in general haulage with W.Seward & Son at Petersfield, Hants, before going into show business, but during the winter of 1938/39 it was converted to a full show engine, handsomely painted, with dynamo bracket, full length awning, and twisted brass. The outbreak of war on September, 1939, put an end to its London area travels. It reappeared briefly with Maurice Stokes based on its home town of Basingstoke, and then vanished for good.

In the mid-thirties steam was being abandoned very quickly by the owners of shooters, juveniles, hooplas, and the like. It held on rather longer with operators of big rides but leading showmen owning major machines demonstrated a change of heart by going in for purpose-built diesel tractors. John Hoadley, for instance, attracted a lot of attention when he ordered a Scammell tractor to go with his new Moon-rocket ride delivered in 1937. Goodyear, who had supplied the tyres for it, featured it with John posed in front, in their house magazine which they gave away to the trade. Billy Nichols' handsome Foden diesel tractor bought about the same time attracted less publicity, but had a working life of over forty years. Botton Brothers and Bob Wilson each had an E.R.F., probably among the best looking motors ever built for showmen. Despite these defections to diesels some of the leading men in the business still had studs of steam engines. Of these the leading exemplar was Pat Collins of Bloxwich, but another prominent operator of the steam engine was Alfred Deakin of Brynmawr who had the last Burrell showman's engine to be built (No. 4092 of 1930). He would also have had the final Fowler showman (No.20223 of 1934), the celebrated *Supreme,* but died before it was delivered. It was, however, operated by his widow and sons, who continued the business. For a showman from the Welsh mining valleys to run a coal fired steam engine was perhaps, in many ways, a gesture of solidarity with the mining fraternity from which he drew so many of his customers. Showmen with more nebulous connections with mining understandably felt less inhibited.

The second rank men were in a different case. Most of the larger engines owned by them were second or third-hand at or near the end of their lives whilst, as we have seen, steam wagons had largely been dispensed with already in favour of lorries or old buses, and tractors were being thinned out year by year, often after very short lives. Purchase's *Wallace,* for example, new to them in 1910, was last licensed in 1926 after passing to Frank Davis of Bexhill, Sussex. With no new engines being built the only way the stock could be augmented was by conversions from road haulage engines. In the thirties a number of road engines came onto the market which, though old or relatively old, had been well maintained and lightly worked. The Aveling & Porter 8NHP No.4885 *Samson* of 1901 had spent the greater part of its life attached to Chatham Dockyard. When it was retired in 1935 it was snapped up by Charles Presland for use in his round of Essex grounds until superseded by *Princess Mary* (Burrell No.3949). Another engine which entered the amusement business about the same time was Burrell 8NHP No.2342, new in 1900 to Halifax Gasworks, and, rather earlier, Fowler No.9456 of 1902, formerly the property of W.Arnold & Sons of East Peckham, Kent. The former was purchased and converted by Robert Body of Meopham, Kent, and the latter by Frank Harris of Flimwell who, c.1935, named it *Marina* in honour of the Greek princess who was then newly married to the Duke of Kent. In 1946 it passed to Tom Smith of Shoreham to replace Foden No.528.

Despite these engines being about thirty years old when they were converted they gave on average about a dozen years service to their new owners, but the artificial conditions induced by the second war helped to extend their lives in a way that cannot readily be evaluated. Why they were converted so late and why

Fig.135. Fowler No.12255 Princess *heads the road train of its owner, R.Townsend of Weymouth.*

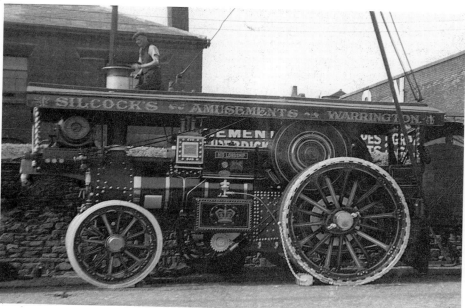

Fig.136. Silcock's His Lordship *(Burrell No. 3444 of 1913 - new to John Green of Preston),specially spruced up for the Coronation in 1937.*

Fig.137. *(bottom) Bostock & Wombwell's Robey tractor No.37660,* Bengal, *in Boothferry Road, Hull, for the Show's last appearance at Hull Fair, October 12, 1931. [J.L.Middlemiss collection]*

a trickle of conversions continued until 1945/46, when Allan Downs converted the Fowler No.10182, is a question that defies a single, all-embracing answer. The motives of showpeople are as complex and diverse as those of any other segment of our society. Personal preference or an affinity for steam are doubtless the whole explanation in some cases. The Roses, for instance, have kept their Foster *Maude* (No. 3642 of 1908) against all commercial blandishments, simply because they are very attached to the engine. Certainly personal preference accounts for Allan Downs' late use of steam. Once electricity had come upon the scene a constant power source was imperative, even more so when the riding machines themselves were electrified. As a generator the steam engine was profoundly reliable and governed well. Nothing, it is true, could stop the lights dimming a little and the organ slowing slightly as a big ride was set on the move, but for the majority of fairground proprietors the steam engine, of whatever type, was a more reliable source of electricity than the general run of petrol engined internal combustion vehicles available to them in the twenties, with the honorable exception of the Tilling Stevens petrol electrics, already mentioned, which were noted for reliability. At every large fair in the thirties bevies of these could be seen soldiering on hour after hour with radiators on or near the boil.

A machine owner simply could not afford to have his power supply give out on him, for without the machine running his income was cut off, and therefore what he desired in a generator, almost above all else, was reliability. This characteristic was one in which steam engines excelled. Even when worn in every part they would continue to function. Apart from dropping the plug or having a tube burst or pinhole, there was not much that would stop a steam engine, barring a catastrophic breakage, which was rare. If the fair opened at 2p.m. and closed at 11p.m. there might be one stop for oiling up the big ends and eccentrics about tea-time, but otherwise it would be running continuously. An engine thus running required an attendant who never dared be far away in case the governor belt broke or came off. In many cases this meant the owner or one of his sons being there, whilst his wife or some other member of the family took care of the pay-box. When this was not possible or where the owner had more than one engine paid drivers filled the gap, and these came in rich variety.

Many were known by nicknames. Alfie Banks who drove Ling's Fowler *The Gladiator* was generally known as 'Little Punch' whilst John Harvey who was often to be seen at the controls of Pat Collins' *No.1* was usually called 'Cockney Jack', for fairly obvious reasons. Other topographical nicknames were those of Tom McIntosh ('Gateshead Tommy'), driver of Irvin's Fowler *One of the Best*, and Bob Gault ('Scotch Bob') who worked for Bostock & Wombwell's menagerie. A less than flattering nickname was that of 'Greasy Tommy' who worked for the Harniess family on the single crank compound Burrell *Perseverance*.

Two well-known and well liked London drivers were Billy Stevens who had many seasons with the late George Irvin's Foster *Marvel* and 'Yiewsley Jack' (John Denahy, 1904-1989) who was often to be seen on the William Beach engines and was the old gentleman's grandson-in-law. Jack was one of several children of a swillman employed by Squires, the trout farmers at Yiewsley, to make a night-time collection of swill from the hotels, clubs and restaurants of the West End. With his father poorly paid and anyway overfond of beer it was his mother who was the pivot of the household. When Jack was about eleven she died, and the family structure collapsed, the children being taken into orphanages. The regimented life of an institution did not suit Jack, who soon arranged his permanent absence. Being a strong, cheerful and adaptable lad, mature for his age, he turned to fairgrounds. He was fortunate enough to find a niche with the Beachs and was with them on a more or less regular basis for several years. One day he was sent for by William Beach. "It's come to my ears that you are dating our Lina" he charged Jack, who could not deny it. As Jack said when relating the story "I was probably about 15 and she was about 12, but I still had to go". The rule was, and mostly still is, that gaff lads do not cast their eyes upon showmen's daughters, and though old William did it with real regret he sent Jack packing. Jack worked as a steam driver with the firms in the Middlesex ballast trade and in general cartage work. Despite the fact that men were taken on and stood off as business fluctuated, as he was a good driver he was rarely out of employment. He and Selina never gave up even in the face of the discouragements she received at home. Eventually her father gave in, and she and Jack were married in 1931. Jack had many adventures with the Beach engines, but possibly the most startling was the day *Conqueror* (Burrell No.2116 of 1898) broke the rear axle in Osnaburgh Street (just east of Regents Park) whilst leading the loads away from the 1919 Worlds Fair held that year in Cumberland Market because the Agricultural Hall was not available. Jack was on the engine with William Beach, Senior, when it happened. The sett paving in Osnaburgh Street was blamed but Jack put the real cause down to an old flaw.

Fig.138. Though no picture is known to exist of Conqueror *after the axle broke in Osnaburgh Street, this one shows a Burrell (said to have been Mrs.Holland's No.3093) in a similarly embarassing situation. [Allan Downs' collection]*

Fig.139. (centre) Teddy Andrews' Aveling & Porter tractor Jessie, *(No.8885).*

Fig.140. (bottom) Burrell 6NHP road loco No.3489, new in 1913 to J.W.Ponsford & Son of Topsham, Devon. Later, when with J.Hickey & Son of Richmond it was one of the engines in the celebrated accident at Cobham with the Hackbridge transformer Soon after it was sold to Swales Bolesworth and by him in 1938 to Teddy Andrews, in whose hands it was in the picture.

On one occasion Goldthorpe Marshall had attended Bridlington October Fair with his Proud Peacock ride and after pulling down was faced with driving his Fowler (No.10329 *Envoy* of 1905) on the 100 miles trip over the Pennines to Kendal for the November Fair. Though the Fowler was master of its loads the engine hauling the other loads (Burrell No.3787 *Thomas William* of 1918) was floundering on the steeper grades and repeatedly he had to scotch up his own loads and go back as pilot to the other engine. Finally as they pulled off for the night at Clapham the ground collapsed under the Fowler and it came to rest in a cellar. Many other twentieth century showmen who were proficient drivers handled their own engines or entrusted them to members of the family. When it is considered that the engines, rides, and owner's living wagon might have been bought with the accumulated savings of a lifetime of sustained effort and represented their owner's entire capital it is not surprising that he wished to take good care of it. Owner drivers or drivers from major ride owners' families included Ernest Emerson, Fred Waddington, Jimmy and Billy Crow, Roland Tucker, Allan Downs, William and John Shaw, and George Irvin. The list is illustrative and not exhaustive. Amongst the owners of round stalls and side-stuff it was rare to find a paid driver in charge, as much from the pressure of economics as from any other reason.

Among the paid drivers there were also men of very high skills. Tom Glover, for instance, was a very fine man, capable, intelligent, wise in the ways of engines, long-sighted and seldom known to have been wrong footed by a sudden emergency. He had many seasons in charge of Green's Burrell *His Majesty* (No.3089) but had driven also for Frank Sedgwick and other showmen. There were also some incompetents, witness Frank Cheffins' account of what he found when he took charge of Burrell No.4000, *Ex Mayor,* for Harry Tuby at Epworth, Yorkshire.

> "At six years old, she ought to have been in good nick, but I am afraid that this was not the case. For those who are not very conversant with work on the Tobers, engines often tend to run in somewhat poor condition. It is not always possible to wash out boilers when required, or attend to bearing adjustment when it becomes necessary. An engine has to be kept going at all costs for it is the ride that is the most important thing, the engine is only there because of the ride. This may prove to be a costly exercise in the long run, but often a riding master has no choice; he cannot afford to have his machine laid up, so the engine has to be often 'jollied along' until there is time to attend to it.
>
> So far as I was concerned I knew all about the troubles with *Ex Mayor,* but I had set my heart on driving her. When Harry sent for me to meet him at Epworth I knew I had a hard job ahead of me. The firebox was bad, and the tubes all leaked, there was steam leaking from most of the glands too, and she had not been washed out for weeks. I was ready to cope with all that, and was trained to do so; my chief worry was "Can I really drive her?"

Though many of these drivers, whether family or hired, were authentic characters most were masters of their exacting trade. The forward vision on a showman's engine is distinctly tubular. There is a very long expanse of engine terminating in the bulk of the bracket and dynamo, swaddled against the entry of grit and weather. On a left-hand steered engine - that is all Burrells, Fosters, and the last four Fowlers - the driver could rely on his steersman to watch the gutter and the kerb whilst he watched oncoming traffic and kept an eye on the loads, but on a right-hand engine the steerer could not see the nearside of the road and the driver had to keep him informed of what was coming up. The loads were braked individually, usually by a gaff lad riding on them, and there was a communication cord to a gong under the roof of the engine on the back of the nameboard. One ring was the signal to stop and two meant "proceed". Conversely a single blast on the engine's whistle was the signal to the men on the packing trucks to brake and two to take the brakes off.

In the early days of steam haulage with everything on steels, speeds were necessarily low. Many of the vehicles were the legacy of the horse-haulage days, on wooden wheels, steel tyred, and with cast-iron bushes in the wooden naves. The lubrication of such wheels was hardly sufficient to withstand the speed of an engine without overheating. From time to time a bush, having become loose in the wooden nave, would rotate and soon cause smouldering of the wood, a risk requiring constant vigilance on the road. Because many individual loads were small they were necessarily numerous. The much quoted testimonial letter from William Murphy to John Fowler & Co. under the date of November 28, 1895, refers to his road train of ten vehicles. Such a train must have been extremely difficult to manage on the road, and in town streets the rear could have been out of sight of the engine. Even if braked evenly, which was difficult to achieve, such a train would be at risk from jack-knifing if the tyres struck on a greasy patch of setts or on a smooth manhole cover. Despite the superior qualities of solid rubber tyres on hard roads travellers took a long time to overcome their distrust of them, fearing that on grass, where so much of their work lay, they would suffer from lack of adhesion. Confidence in rubbers gained ground after the 1914-18 war and they became virtually compulsory in 1927.

Fig. 141. George Irvin's *Foster* (No.12499 of 1910) *Marvel (on left) and Pat Collins' 10NHP McLaren No.1599* Samson *on Wormwood Scrubs.* Samson *was an ex-War Department engine.*

Fig.142. An offside view of George Irvin's other Foster Marvellous *(No.14057 of 1914). Billy Stevens, the driver, stands by the centre of the rear wheel and his wife in front of the belly tank with their son and daughter between them. Note the unusual geared up drive to the dynamo.*

Fig.143. An engine that entered fairground use late in life was Charles Presland's *Samson (Aveling & Porter No.4885). Built in 1901, it worked until 1935 in Chatham Dockyard but was sold in that year to Charles Presland and used in his round of fairs in South Essex. It is seen here in 1969 when owned by Tom Paisley.*

The Road Vehicles (Showman's Tractors & Heavy Locomotives) Regulations 1927 did not actually forbid steel wheels. Showmen had long argued that as, relative to similar vehicles in other hands, theirs did low mileages on the road each year they should pay less road tax. This was agreed by the Government subject to the condition that such vehicles should be fitted with smooth, continuous rubber tyres. There was, therefore, a very real financial inducement to make the change. Older engines were rubbered, mostly peripherally, with bolt-on tyres, though some owners tried rubber cross strakes, but there were steel-straked engines that never came out again in showland use and were either sold into agricultural work, abandoned, or scrapped.

The regulation produced some weird and wonderful tyres. Michael Salmon summed up the stuation thus:
> "The regulations required that the rubber tyres should extend round the wheels with any gaps in them not exceeding 3in. in the aggregate, i.e. ½in. gaps between the ends of five sections would do, whereas the strakes had nearly the total gap between each strake, although it was argued that the slope of the strakes ensured that rubber was on the road all the time at some point across the wheel. A number of showman's engines were shod with rubber strakes; Messrs. Llewellyn of Ross-on-Wye advertised their capacity for doing the work, and some owners did them themselves. At least one engine was fitted with a combination of continuous bands on the outside of the wheel and small rubber strakes up the middle, but instead of the best of both worlds the spaces filled with mud and they lost their effectiveness. This was the Fowler *King Edward VII* of Whittles of Camberley, later owned by Mr.A.Napper. The last working showman's engine to be fitted with rubber strakes is believed to have been the big Foster road loco owned by Mr.Arthur Traylen, the West London showman. This engine wore out her continuous tyres early in the second world war [I think it was earlier. Philip Bradley photographed her on cross strakes in September, 1938. R.A.W.] and was then fitted with rubber strakes, but as the rubber used was very narrow they gave a very rough ride."

This was Foster 14381, *Queen Mary*. The sensation described by Michael's phrase "a very rough ride" was put to the author rather more forcefully by Frank Seaton, who drove the engine and helped to fit the strakes, as "Like riding on a bloody cog wheel."

The big engines built new during the twenties and early thirties all came out new on solid rubbers. These were the Burrell Scenics and the Fowler Lions and Big Lions, all really fast. Jack Wilkinson paced a Big Lion on its way to Hull Fair with three heavy Dodgem loads, one of which was the plate truck, carrying the steel floor plates of the ride, for miles at a time at 18m.p.h., a speed that would have been out of the question on steel tyres. Though such a rate of travel shortened journey times it also increased the strain on the driver and steersman, making the co-ordination between the engineman and the brakesmen very important, and the timing extremely critical.

Most hired drivers lived away from the fairground. Gaffs and casuals might doss in the packing trucks but generally drivers went for lodgings. Many pubs and beer houses provided accommodation for working men and plenty of householders and cottagers took in lodgers. On the whole engine drivers were not a favourite type of lodger though perhaps looked at less askance in a steel-making or mining area, where people tended to take a blackened face more for granted than in other places. Elsewhere they often had to accept dubious lodgings. How hard this came to them varied from individual to individual. To a man like Frank Cheffins, the son of a farmer and used to a good home life, rough digs would have come harder than to a man born to squalor. Council houses of the twenties, in which a fixed bath was installed in the kitchen, provided with hot water from a copper, were considered (and were) a notable contribution to better living. Most families had to cope by using a zinc bath by the kitchen fire, a privilege that did not, as a rule, extend to the lodger, in the house for only two or three days. A driver could, if he wished, draw a bucket of hot water through the injector and strip off for a sluice in an empty truck or, again, in most larger towns there were public bath-houses.

There was, however, a sizeable residue of drivers who slept rough on the fairground. One man is said to have slept on a board laid on the motion of the engine. Others slept under the engine or in a truck. Of this brigade those who had a partiality for beer formed a substantial part. A man with a twelve pint thirst tended to find it convenient not to be too closely confined during the night, nor did he make very good company, even by the standard of rough digs. Then again, those who did not care over much for washing often found it convenient to lodge in the open.

Life is not made up solely of beds and ablutions and nor were all landladies bad. The anecdotes of any men, not only showmen's drivers, who followed itinerant occupations in the twenties and thirties, are usually droll in the extreme and often able to hold an audience in stitches, especially after a couple of rounds of beer, but their fabric is of meetings with old friends and mates; of the eccentricities of employers - unless the narrator was an employer, in which case he probably recalls the peculiarities of the

Fig.144. Fowler's version of the 'Scenic', built in 1923, was essentially a Class R3 road locomotive with a much extended smokebox to carry the exciter. Given the number 15658 and named His Lordship, it went to Simons & Teago of Caernarvon but, in practice, was found to be over-long for handling in awkward or constricted situations.

Fig.145. By contrast, Harry Tuby's Ex-Mayor (Burrell No.4000 of 1925), though a large and powerful engine is much more compact. Here it is pictured at Barnby Dun near Doncaster on July 2, 1934, by Jack Wilkinson. [A.J.Martin collection]

Fig.146. Though Burrell tractorNo.3868 (1920) was new to George Baker of Southampton, it is best remembered in the hands of Arnold Brothers on the Isle of Wight. Unlike many fairground tractors it was on rubbers from new.

gaffs - the shortcomings and merits of steersmen; hurried build-ups and frenzied pull-downs; heroic treks (such as Nottingham Goose Fair to Hull); encounters with constables; mishaps on the road; impromptu repairs; failure of water supplies; and, sometimes, of accident and real tragedy. An afternoon, thirty years ago, spent with Tom Glover was punctuated with such stories. The life was undoubtedly quite unlike anything to be encountered today, but most lived it with gusto and the few survivors look back with relish. Balmy summer nights and harvest moons are remembered; pull-downs when water oozed from the lace-holes of the boots are forgotten. If the price of being twenty-five again were no more than a wet shirt, who would demur?

After 1918 the total of 7 and 8NHP Burrells delivered, including the Leiston built *Simplicity* was only thirty-four plus Tuby's *Ex Mayor*, with 10NHP cylinders, and a further nine of 5 and 6NHP. Fowlers' score in the same period was sixteen and Fosters' nineteen. The Tuby firm had *Ex Mayor* built with every improvement that they had looked for and found wanting in an engine of standard specification. The major differences, however, lay in the use of 10NHP cylinders (7¼in. and 11¾in. x 12in.) in place of the 8NHP cylinders mounted on the majority of scenics (6¾in. and 11¼in. x 12in.), and the feature that distinguished it most from its contemporaries, namely its reversion to the 1905 arrangement of single drive and a differential on the nearside end of the driven axle with the roping drum. This layout, in combination with narrow rear wheels, reduced the overall width of the engine to suit some of the congested sites that it had to visit, and, furthermore, enabled much greater rear axle spring travel to be accommodated. In short, the Tubys had set out to have an engine with the best features afforded by contemporary road locomotive design with the addition of certain characteristics to suit their particular needs. In practice these special features never yielded the satisfaction that had been looked for. Some were set at nought by the indefinable and, in some ways, inexplicable malaise that seemed to hover over the works at Thetford in the terminal AGE days of the firm. Others had been defeated by the incompetence of the men paid to drive the engine.

Fortune tends to pay only fickle court to the fairground. In 1910, the year King George V and Queen Mary came to the throne, it seemed to be in a smiling mood. Fairs were widely held and properous, the mobile bioscope shows were at their peak and massive new riding machines were pulling ever increasing crowds to the major fairs - large new four-abreast gallopers, razzle-dazzles and, in 1910 itself, the electric scenic railway. With a height of 20 feet and an overall diameter of 55 feet a scenic was a formidable machine, driven by electricity throughout. Two hills, eight cars each weighing a ton, an ornate organ in the centre, with perhaps a waterfall as well, added up to a machine that used a lot of current. In practice it also created a peak load problem on starting which was solved by the ingenuity of Messrs. L.A.Hackett and E.W.Whatman who between them invented the scenic engine with its twin dynamos, the main one on the front bracket, and the auxiliary - to provide the current to excite the coils of the main dynamo - mounted between the cylinder block and the chimney.

Whatman worked for Fosters of Lincoln and consequently the first engines to be supplied like this were of the Foster '65 BHP' series, but after Whatman and Fosters had become disenchanted with each other, and he had removed his talents to other spheres, viz. boot and shoe machinery, Burrells let it be known that they were keen to join the fray, and subsequently forty-three Burrell engines were built or rebuilt as scenics. Fowlers, offering as they did four shaft engines, were not able to provide the space on the boiler top for the auxiliary, though they did build No.15658 (1923) with a very extended smokebox on which the smokestand was placed between the main dynamo bracket and the stand for the auxiliary. The result had a distinctly uncomely air, and mostly they used their earlier and simpler solution of putting the auxiliary on the gear side front tank with its drive pulley looking inwards so that a diagonal drive could be arranged to the main generator. One of the engines so arranged was F.Cox's *Adjutant* (No. 14847 of 1920) driven over a number of seasons by George Lee who lived to see, and take part in, the earlier years of the rally movement.

The first scenic railway was ordered by Enoch Farrar, the celebrated and rugged Yorkshire showman who had a circuit of grounds in industrial Yorkshire and Nottinghamshire. The ride was undoubtedly a powerful attraction and in the next three years other leading riding masters ordered rides each a little more impressive than the previous one. Despite its great pulling power and high riding capacity a scenic railway had drawbacks. A substantial proportion of its potential earnings was earmarked to service the high capital cost of the ride and its road locomotives. Secondly, it took a lot of labour for building up and pulling down, although pre-1914 such labour was cheap and plentiful. Thirdly, few owners of scenics

Figs.147 and 148. Two photographs by Robert Pratt are nostalgic of fairground steam in the 1930's. Above, Arthur Greenway stands by the rear wheel of Fowler No.14412 (later owned by Allan Downs) during a water stop on the way to Aldeburgh Regatta fair.
Below, J.Rowland & Son's Garrett (No.33739) heads their road train through a Cornish village on a sunlit June day.

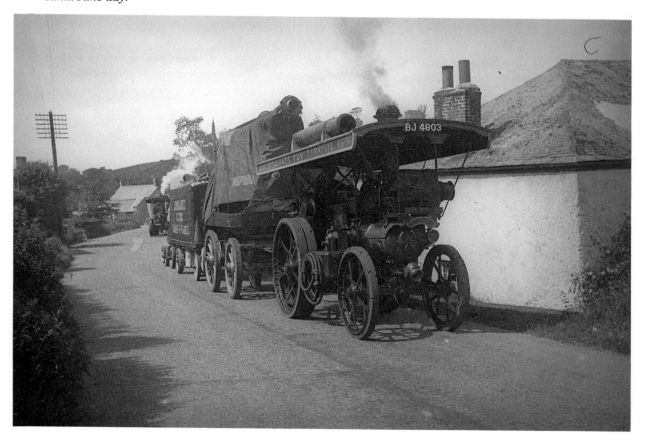

could keep them provided continuously with sites of sufficient earning potential. Furthermore no one could guarantee good weather. So the scenic rides rolled in the pennies when the site was right, and the weather was fine, but on second-rate pitches or in bad weather there was not enough income though the heavy overhead continued. By the late twenties or early thirties, when the novelty had worn off, many scenics had been settled on static grounds at the bigger seaside resorts. Others had been left in the yards whilst more manageable machines, such as swirls, dodgems, or the smaller arks, took to the road. The war had totally altered the casual labour supply, and no longer were there men willing to work all night for a shilling. This had hit all machine owners but especially the owners of scenic railways.

The decline of the popularity of the scenic railway was paralleled by the eclipse of its makers, Savages Ltd. of Kings Lynn, as the leading makers of riding machines. Their pre-eminence in building fairground machinery simply dissolved and was shared amongst other firms - Orton & Spooner of Burton-on-Trent, Lakin of Streatham, and Maxwells of Musselburgh, for example. The trend towards all electric drives continued. The travelling of the newly popular dodgems and speedways on the road was made possible by the availability of the efficient generating capacity of the engines developed for use with scenics. These rides appealed to the post-1918 generation of fair-goers, so that although scenic railways themselves had soon faded from the scene and spoiled more fortunes than they made for showmen, the trend towards the novel machines which they ushered in continued unabated until the slump began to bite.

Unfortunately the fairground trade had its strongest roots in the industrial areas of South Wales, the Midlands, the North of England and Lowland Scotland. Coal mining areas declined first, followed by steel making, heavy engineering, shipbuilding, and the cotton and woollen districts but, on the other hand, prosperity in the areas in which the motor industry had settled - the Black Country and Oxford - grew, as it did on the whole in the South and South-East. After 1925, the three famous makers, Burrell, Foster, and Fowler, between them produced only four big engines. When the trade revived post-slump, travellers renewing their haulage plant looked to motors.

Perhaps the most inspiring spectacle that the era of steam transport on the fairground afforded was that of a Burrell scenic, on pressed-on rubbers, hurrying the big packing trucks of a dodgem ride through the warmth of a summer night. Sadly it had a very short currency. Almost as soon as it had become established on the scene it was beginning to bow off again. But whilst it lasted it was a picture not easily to be forgotten.

Fig.149. Charles Presland's Princess Mary *(Burrell No.3949) and* Medina *(Garrett tractor No.33902) at the* Ship & Shovel, *Barkingside, Essex. The former previously belonged to Wm.Nichols and* Medina *to James Humphreys.*   [Philip Bradley]

138